WIRING FOR THE
DO-IT-YOURSELFER

4

Table of Contents

INTRODUCTION

You don't have to be a genius to do many basic wiring jobs around your home, whether just for routine maintenance or to increase the convenience and value of your home. All you need are a few tools and the ability to follow step-by-step instructions. This book shows you just how easy it can be. It also gives you important tips that will make your wiring work safe and easy. First, a little background ...

THE ELECTRICAL SYSTEM

The electricity in your home starts at a power generating plant and is sent at high voltage to distribution stations. Then it's transmitted through conductors to local areas, where it is transformed to a lower voltage and branches off into wires leading to individual buildings.

The two most common types of wiring systems which may lead into your home are two-wire and three-wire. Your home's wiring could be either, depending on local requirements at the time it was built.

WHAT IS "POLARIZATION"?

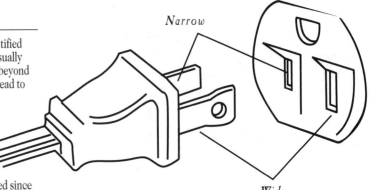

Narrow

Wide

A. The National Electrical Code requires that home wiring be identified by color code. Neutral wires are white; live wires are colored, usually black or red. Polarization is a method to continue this identity beyond the outlet to the live and neutral wires in an extension cord or lead to a lamp, appliance or other home electrical product. It assures that the live lead is connected to the incoming side of the switch in the appliance.

Wide and narrow prongs on a polarized plug match wide and narrow slots in the outlet. The wide slot in the outlet is connected to the neutral (white) wire in the electrical system. All grounding (3-prong) plugs are polarized since the position of the prongs is determined by the third prong. In polarized lamp and appliance leads and extension cords, the neutral (white) wire may be "ribbed" for identification.

Q. *Why is this alignment of the prongs important?*

A. This is to assure that in electrical wiring and appliances the switch is in the hot (black) wire. Thus wiring and components beyond the switch are not live when the switch is OFF. This eliminates a potential safety hazard created when someone concludes that there is no shock hazard if the switch is off and touches a live part. A fault might also develop within an ungrounded appliance which would make it dangerous to touch exposed metal portions of the appliance. In the case of changing a light bulb, the metal screw shell of the bulb could be live and present a shock hazard if the lamp were not polarized and the switch were not in the live or black wire. (See illustration).

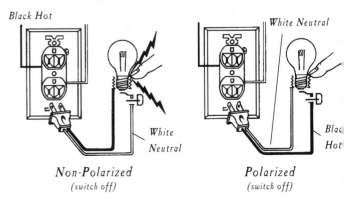

Black Hot

White Neutral

White Neutral

Black Hot

Non-Polarized
(switch off)

Polarized
(switch off)

8

Q. Wouldn't such a fault blow a fuse or trip a breaker?

A. In an ungrounded appliance probably not. Such a "hot" appliance would be a hazard to a person who touched it while also touching a ground, such as a water faucet, a grounded appliance or being in contact with damp ground.

Q. Is polarization a new idea?

A. No. Most wall outlets have been polarized since the 1930's. Grounding plugs have always been polarized.

Q. Are GE extension cords polarized?

A. Yes. GE manufactures only polarized household cord sets. Since 1981, only polarized cordsets received a UL listing. However, GE standardized on polarized cordsets well in advance of this date because of the added safety they provide and their future usefulness as more and more electrical products are furnished with polarized plugs.

Q. How widespread is the use of polarized plugs?

A. Polarized plugs are required on all lamps and many tools, TV sets, radios and appliances presently manufactured.

Q. Can I use non-polarized extension cords with these new products?

A. NO! Never try to force a polarized plug into a non-polarized outlet or cord set. That not only destoys the safety feature of polarization, but may create other hazards, such as live prongs remaining partially exposed, or poor contact being made resulting in overheating.

Q. How about products with non-polarized plugs? Can they be used with new; polarized cord sets?

A. Yes. Any two-wire non-polarized plug can be used with a polarized outlet or cordset. However, there is no safety improvement provided in this case since polarization continuity is not assured throughout the system.

Q. Does GE have other polarized devices in the Wiring Device line?

A. Yes. Our Grounding Triple Tap (GE 1740), Grounding Adapter (GE 4391), Heavy Duty Attachment Plug (GE 4384), Socket Adapter (GE 4310) and Twin Taps (GE 1706 and GE 1707) are all polarized.

GE 1740   GE 4384   GE 4391

GE 4310   GE 1707   GE 1706

9

THE ELECTRICAL SYSTEM

Two-wire

Many small homes built before 1940 have two-wire systems. If this is the case in your home, electricity flows to the house on two wires. The wires transmit 115 volts from a pole or underground cable to the meter, continue to the main power panel or fuse box and then run Through your house.

One wire is the neutral - it's white and is usually grounded at the main power panel by attaching it to the metal water supply or code-approved ground rod where it enters the house. It carries current, so be careful. The other wire (the black one) also has current and is known as the hot or live wire.

A house with the two-wire system may only provide 30 amps or 3,600

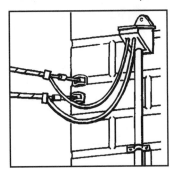

watts of power. That may not be enough power to operate air conditioners, TV's, power tools and other appliances at the same time. In this case you should consider getting a licensed electrical contractor to update your system. Not only will an upgrade make your home more enjoyable but you'll be increasing its value. So look at any expenses as an investment.

Three-wire

Most houses now use the three-wire system because it provides both 115 and 230 volts, giving you just about complete freedom to use any size appliance, including electric ranges and dryers.

Of the three wires entering a house, two are live and the other is the grounded neutral wire. In the main panel the neutral is usually white or bare and the live or hot wires are usually black and red. The three wires are connected to the meter, then go to the fuse or circuit breaker panel where they branch into separate circuits.

Here's how you get both 115- and 230-volt power from one set of wires. You'll find 115-volt power available between a black or red wire and the

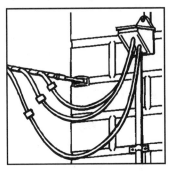

neutral wire. You'll find 230-volt power available between the red and the black wire for appliances such as ranges, dryers and large air conditioners.

Present three-wire systems are usually rated 100- or 150-amps. If you have electric heat, you might even have more power coming into your home.

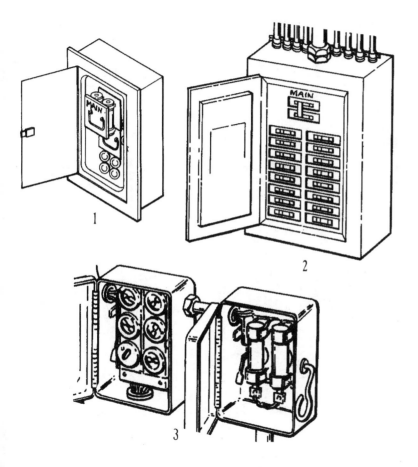

1

2

3

THE ELECTRICAL SYSTEM

Main power panels

There are times when you need to shut off power for the entire house - when working inside the fuse or breaker panel or in the case of emergency, such as a fire or basement flooding. it may not be required but that's why you should have a single main switch or circuit breaker at your main panel. If you don't have one, don't try to put one in yourself. This is one type of home wiring job that is better left to a qualified electrician.

Ordinarily, main and branch fuses or breakers are in the some metal box. However, the main disconnect switch or breaker may be in a separate box. Wherever it is, you are able to operate it without being exposed to live wires.

Three types of main power disconnects used are (1) fused pull-out, (2) circuit breaker and (3) lever. In many older houses you pull a lever and this shuts off all power. You also have to pull the handle to get to the fuses, which protects you when you change a fuse.

11

THE ELECTRICAL SYSTEM

Branch circuits

A branch circuit is all the wiring controlled by the same fuse or circuit breaker. You can see where each circuit begins by looking at the wires running out of the fuse or circuit breaker box.

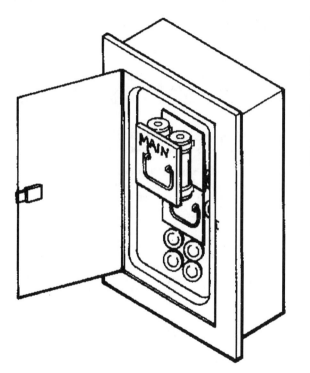

THE ELECTRICAL SYSTEM

Many houses have cartridge fuses mounted in an insulated pull-out. When the pull-out is removed, power to that circuit is shut off. One pullout may be used as a main for total power shutdown. There may be a separate pull-out for other high current appliances, such as a range or dryer.

To replace a fuse, remove the pull-out. To reconnect power, push the pull-out back into place. If it's inserted upside down, it won't reconnect.

In circuit breaker panels with a main breaker, you'll see a large (100A or larger) on/off breaker for the main disconnect. To shut off all power, you just switch it to its "off" position.

THE ELECTRICAL SYSTEM

Fuses

A fuse is one of the most common types of protective devices in older homes. Inside the fuse, electricity flows through a metal strip that's designed to melt and break the circuit when too many amps go through it. An overloaded circuit (too many appliances plugged in) is one way a fuse will blow. Another way is when wires in the circuit cross or a live wire touches a neutral wire or is grounded. A fuse that is loose in its socket may overheat and blow, too.

If a fuse blows and you don't know the cause, you can sometimes identify the type of failure by looking at the fuse. If there's a short somewhere the gloss window will usually be discolored by the blowing of the strip and you might not even see the strip inside. But if the circuit is overloaded, the strip may melt with little or no discoloration to the window and will remain visible through the window.

Some of the most common types of fuses are: plug, non-tamperable, time delay and cartridge. The National Electrical Code now prohibits installing plug fuses (sometimes called Edison base fuses) in new homes. They're too easy to misuse by installing ones with higher amperage ratings than is safe for your home's wiring. This can be prevented by installing adapters and converting to "Type S" fuses.

Non-tamperable fuses (Type S) were designed to prevent using a fuse rated higher than the size for which the circuit was wired. They use adapters for each fuse size that cannot be removed once put in. The adapters prevent substitution of a higher-rated fuse - for example, a 30-amp fuse won't fit a 20-amp adapter.

Some tools and appliances need a short burst of power to start - much more than they take once they get going. During this burst, standard plug-type fuses may repeatedly blow, even though the circuit isn't dangerously overloaded.

Time-delay fuses have a specially designed metal strip that provides for this kind of short overload without interrupting power.

Main power fuses are cartridge fuses. They come in many ratings and are usually installed in pull-outs. Some houses, especially older ones, may also have cartridge fuses for each branch circuit.

THE ELECTRICAL SYSTEM

Short Circuit

Overload

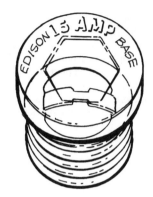

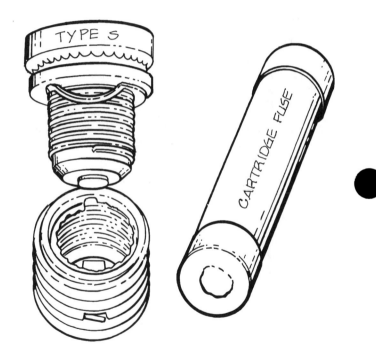

THE ELECTRICAL SYSTEM

Circuit breakers

Another type of circuit protective device is the circuit breaker. Most homes built since the 1950's have circuit breakers instead of fuses.

Common circuit breaker types are switch and push button. Switch type circuit breakers are by far the most popular, three types and ratings of which are shown here. Using toggle handles, they look and work like wall light switches, but the difference is that in case of overload or short circuit, the circuit breaker trips and automatically opens the circuit. To turn the power back on, you have to flip the switch back to "off" or "reset" then to "on".

The push-button type of circuit breaker works just about the same way, only with push-buttons instead of a toggle switch. An overload or short causes the button to stick out. Reset, after solving the problem, by pushing in the button.

There are also circuit breakers that are designed to protect against more than just overloads. They're also designed to protect people against one of the more common types of electrical shock, called "ground faults". If a ground fault occurs, such as from a malfunctioning power tool, the breaker trips in a fraction of a second before most healthy people would get hurt. Ground-fault protection is now required on some circuits in all new construction. It'd be a good idea to replace your existing breakers with these, especially on outdoor circuits or any others that have outlets near water, such as bathrooms and kitchens.

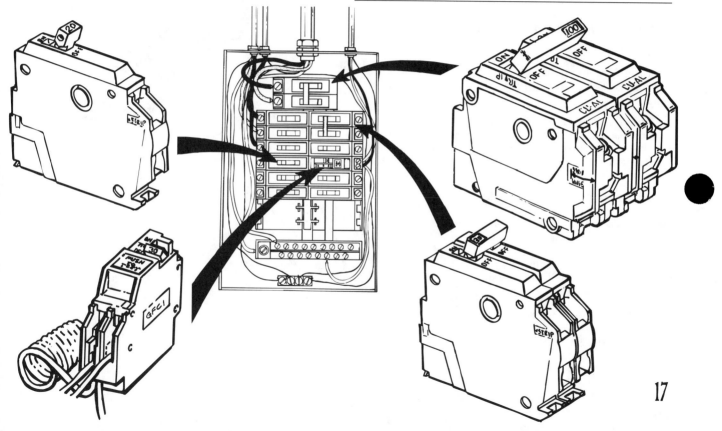

GETTING READY

Before you pick up your first screwdriver, read this:

You should be able to do minor wiring correctly and safely by carefully following the step-by-step instructions in this book and if your existing wiring meets the National Electrical Code and your local code.

This is a very important "if" because the wiring in houses over 25 years old often can't provide enough electricity for today's larger appliances. When this is true, you should consider having a professional rewire your whole system. It's worth the cost and you'll have increased the value of your home by bringing its electrical system up to par with new homes.

In addition, make sure your home's electrical system hasn't been incorrectly rewired, changed or modified by people who lived there before you. For example, they could have tampered with fuses, causing a lack of proper circuit protection. Or there could be the danger of shock if you're working with an appliance that isn't correctly grounded.

If you have any doubt, you may want to have a licensed electrician check to be sure the wiring is adequate and correctly installed.

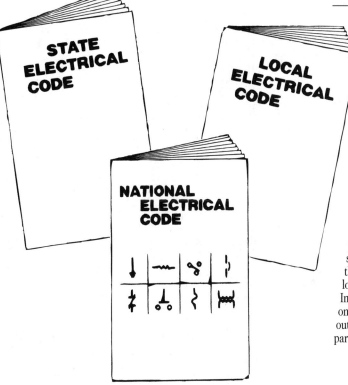

GETTING READY

Why codes?

Codes exist to help you install a safe wiring system. They tell you not only what's right, but also the right materials to use. So before you add or install wiring, or make anything more than a minor repair, contact your local building inspector for the latest local and national code information. Also, you may need a permit for electrical work other than replacing a fixture or switch. If so, when you're finished, your work may be checked for safety by your local electrical inspector.

Buying materials

After determining what materials are needed, select those which include detailed instructions. The manufacturer's instructions may provide even more details or may vary slightly from the information given in this book. In buying electrical devices, look for the Underwriters Laboratories Inc. listing mark (UL). This holds true not only for plugs, connectors, switches, and outlets, but also for wall plates which are also part of the home's electrical system.

GETTING READY

Identifying circuits

Obviously, before you begin wiring, you MUST shut off power to the circuit you're working on. You need to know which fuse or circuit breaker controls each circuit. Here's how to trace circuits.

1. First, turn on (or leave on) the main circuit breaker or switch.

2. Then take out one fuse (or turn one circuit breaker to "off").

3. Turn on all wall switches in your home.

4. Use a circuit tester or plug a small lamp into each outlet to see if the electricity is on.

5. Identify each outlet and light on the shut-off circuit. For future reference, put a label with this information on the door of the box adjacent to that circuit.

6. Switch the breaker to "on" or replace the fuse.

7. For each branch circuit, repeat steps 1-6.

Note: Appliances such as refrigerators, washers, dryers and other large appliances usually have their own separate circuits. Any 230-volt appliances will usually have two fuses or a two-pole breaker, such as is shown in the upper right side of the power panel shown here. Circuits may also have a shared neutral, as in the diagram shown on p. 81.

20

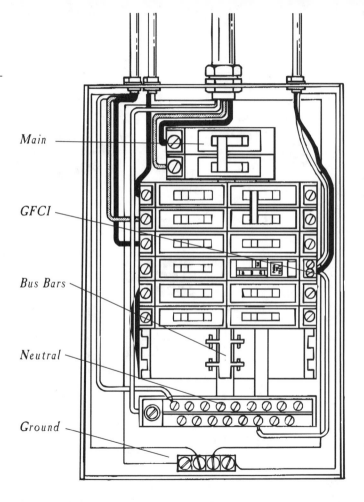

Main

GFCI

Bus Bars

Neutral

Ground

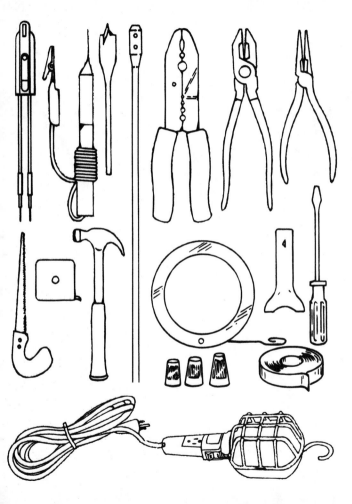

GETTING READY

Tools you should own

In addition to common household tools, such as screwdrivers, saw, hammer, nails and electric drill, these wiring tools will be helpful if you're going to do anything beyond simple replacements:

Drill bits - for extending or relocating circuits, a 3/4-inch spade bit is needed for running through wood floors & studs; a 1/2-inch carbide-tipped masonry kit works for masonry. An extension attachment is needed for thick beams.

Pliers - long-nose pliers to make wire loops & lineman's pliers to pull wire.

Combination tool - crimps, strips wire, also includes wire gauges.

Fish tape - to puff new electrical wire through walls.

Plastic electrical tape and twist-on wire connectors for securing connections without solder.

Continuity tester - working off batteries, it checks for continuity in un-energized circuits.

Circuit tester - Used to determine whether power is flowing through a circuit, as well as if the circuit is properly grounded.

Cable slitter - quickly cuts and removes cable covering without nicking the wire.

Utility light - cord extension and hanger puts light where you need it-provides grounding outlet for a drill or other tool.

21

GETTING READY

Making a good connection

If a few precautions are taken, good connections are easy to make. NOTE: Devices which are UL-Listed for direct connection to aluminum wire have CO/ALR or AL-CU markings as noted below.

Also, be sure to follow any special instructions supplied by the devices' manufacturers.

Binding screw connections

WIRING DEVICES, SWITCHES, RECEPTACLES, LAMP HOLDERS, ETC., WITH BINDING SCREW TERMINALS CANNOT BE CONNECTED DIRECTLY TO ALUMINUM WIRE UNLESS THEY ARE MARKED "CO/ALR". Other type terminals for direct connection to aluminum wire are marked AL-CU...

These steps should be followed for both copper and aluminum wire:

1. Wrap the freshly stripped end of the wire 2/3 to 3/4 of the distance around the wire binding screw as shown in the illustration. The loop is made clockwise so that the rotation of the screw in tightening will tend to wrap the wire around the screw rather than unwrap it.

2. TIGHTEN BINDING SCREWS SECURELY.

Good performance depends upon a tight connection so give the screw an extra twist to be sure it's tight.

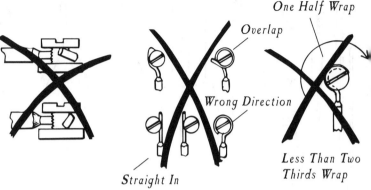

Wrong

One Half Wrap

Overlap

Wrong Direction

Straight In

Less Than Two Thirds Wrap

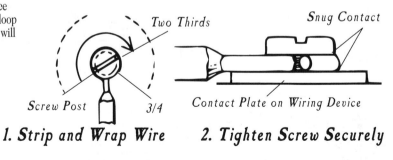

Right

Two Thirds

Snug Contact

Screw Post

3/4

Contact Plate on Wiring Device

1. Strip and Wrap Wire

2. Tighten Screw Securely

22

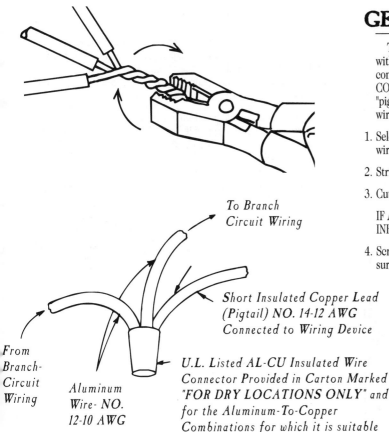

To Branch
Circuit Wiring

Short Insulated Copper Lead
(Pigtail) NO. 14-12 AWG
Connected to Wiring Device

From
Branch-
Circuit
Wiring

Aluminum
Wire- NO.
12-10 AWG

U.L. Listed AL-CU Insulated Wire
Connector Provided in Carton Marked
"FOR DRY LOCATIONS ONLY" and
for the Aluminum-To-Copper
Combinations for which it is suitable

GETTING READY

Twist-on wire connectors are used to join wires in electrical boxes without screws, solder, or crimping. You should use these only where the connections won't be pulled or strained. Wiring devices not marked CO/ALR can be connected to aluminum wire by using a method called "pig-tailing," in which a six-inch piece of copper wire is connected to the wiring device and a twist-on connector* is used as shown.

1. Select the proper size connector for the wires being used. If any of the wires are aluminum, use connectors marked AL-CU.

2. Strip wires approximately 1-1/2 inches and twist together with pliers.

3. Cut off ends of twisted wires to fit twist-on connector.

   IF ALUMINUM WIRE IS BEING USED, APPLY AN OXIDE-INHIBITING COMPOUND.

4. Screw twist-on connectors onto wires. Tighten firmly. Pull on wire to be sure they are secure.

*Connector must be UL Listed
for use with Copper or Aluminum.

23

GETTING READY

Push-in connections

Push-in terminations are found on many wiring devices. This type of termination provides a quick and easy means of terminating copper or copper clad wire. IT SHOULD NOT BE USED FOR ALUMINUM WIRE OR STRANDED CONDUCTORS REGARDLESS OF MATERIAL.

To make connection, strip the wire to the length indicated by the strip gauge on the device - then push the wire into the desired hole. To release, insert a small screwdriver into the release slot.

Heavy duty clamp type terminations

High current (30 amps and over) wiring devices such as range and dryer receptacles requiring heavy gauge wiring employ clamp type terminals rather than binding screws. If the wiring to these devices is aluminum, be sure that the device is rated AL-CU, signifying that it may be used with either copper or aluminum wire. Generally, wire of the size used with these devices is stranded and care should be taken that all strands are inserted into the terminal clamps and tightened securely.

Crimp terminals

Crimp terminals may be used for internal connections in electrical equipment such as furnaces and major appliances. They come in a variety of styles, such as ring and spade type for attaching wires & screw terminals. Male and female disconnect terminals are often used for quick connecting and disconnecting in electrical equipment.

Crimp terminals should be selected to match wire size and application as indicated in instructions provided with the terminals and crimped to the wire with a crimping tool designed for this work- PLIERS SHOULD NEVER BE USED FOR CRIMPING TERMINALS. Completed terminations should be tugged to check for secureness of crimp. These terminals should never be used with aluminum wire.

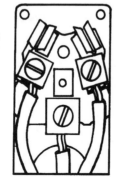

24

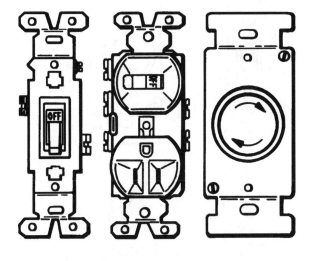

REPLACEMENTS

Some basics

The easiest home wiring jobs are those that involve replacing devices - switches, outlets, circuit breakers and the like. But as the following pages show, there are still some important things to keep in mind.

For instance, you may begin to replace a wall outlet and find that the connections on the new one don't exactly match those on the old. This section will show you what to do. Additional information can be found in the "Circuit Diagrams" section, p. 78.

In fact, once you understand the basics of replacing devices, you'll be able to make changes to upgrade your home electrical system, such as replacing old switches with dimmers; or outlets and circuit breakers with special devices that guard against electrical shock.

There may be more than one circuit in an outlet or switch box. Before replacing device use a circuit tester (p. 65) to make sure all circuits are turned OFF.

25

REPLACING SWITCHES

Switches

Most switches found in the home are either single-pole, three-way, and four-way. See the separate sections for the functions of these various types, and p. 83 for the wiring diagrams.

Most are available in several models - old style "snap" switches, or quiet switches. You may encounter the no-longer manufactured mercury type switch- they may be replaced if needed by the quiet type switch. Switches and dimmers are also available with lighted handles. These require no additional wiring. The lighted handle may be used if you ever need to find a switch in a dark room. They may also be used as a reverse pilot light - the switch handle will be lit when the light being controlled is out. This could be used, for example, to show you in a darkened room that a needed outside light is not on.

Dimmer switches are easy to install and can replace ordinary switches. They can be used to achieve dramatic lighting effects - as well as save energy. Just remember that dimmers for incandescent lights won't work for fluorescent lighting. Special dimmers are available for fluorescent systems, to be used with special ballasts. And don't use dimmers to control outlets or appliances. Overheating might result and that could damage your equipment or the dimmer.

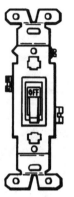

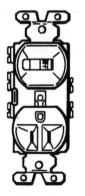

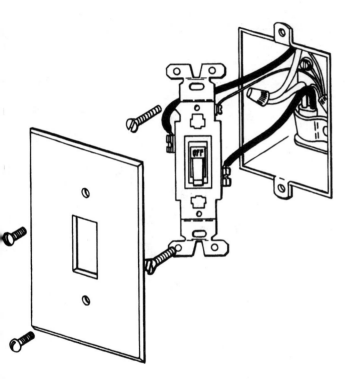

REPLACING SWITCHES

Single-pole

When only one switch controls a light or wall outlet, you have a single-pole switch. They're the easiest switches to replace. These basic instructions will enable you to install any type of switch.

1. REMOVE FUSE OR TURN CIRCUIT BREAKER TO "OFF" BEFORE WIRING.

2. Remove wall plate and old switch.

3. Remove wires from old switch and reconnect to new switch in same manner.

4. Wrap each stripped wire clockwise 3/4 of way around screw. Or solid conductors may be inserted straight into a push-in terminal.

5. If bare (grounding) wire is connected to green hex head screw of old switch, reconnect to green hex head screw on new switch bracket or if no screw exists, fasten to metal box or metal switch bracket.

6. Mount the new switch in the box and replace wall plate.

7. Turn on power.

NOTE: IF YOUR HOME HAS ALUMINUM WIRING, SEE INFORMATION ON PAGE 22.

REPLACING SWITCHES

Three-way

A three-way switch always works with another to control the same light or outlet, usually from opposite ends of a room or from the top and bottom of stairs. They're easy to identify because they have three insulated wires running to them. These instructions apply to all three-way switches. Four-way switches are used with two three-way switches where the light is controlled from more than two locations. See pg. 86 for wiring diagram.

1. REMOVE FUSE OR TURN CIRCUIT BREAKER TO "OFF" BEFORE WIRING.

2. Remove wall plate. DO NOT REMOVE OLD WIRES TO OLD SWITCH BEFORE YOU IDENTIFY.

3. REMOVE WIRE ATTACHED TO COMMON TERMINAL ON OLD SWITCH (screw of a different color from other two or marked common). Connect to common terminal of the new switch.

4. Remove other two wires from old switch. Reconnect to the remaining screws of the new switch.

5. Wrap each stripped wire clockwise 3/4 of way around screw. Or solid conductors may be inserted straight into push-in terminals.

6. If bare (grounding) wire is connected to green hex-head screw of old switch, reconnect to green hex head screw on new switch bracket or if no screw exists, fasten to metal box or metal switch bracket.

7. Mount new switch in the box and replace the wall plate.

8. Turn on power. If switches do not work properly you have probably connected the common wire to the wrong terminal (see p. 85).

NOTE: IF YOUR HOME HAS ALUMINUM WIRING, SEE INFORMATION ON PAGE 22.

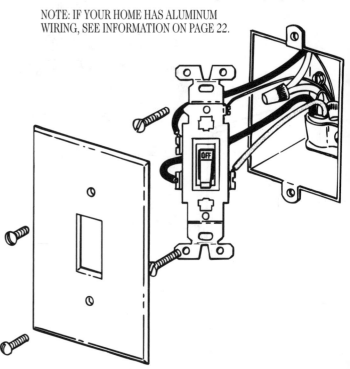

28

REPLACING SWITCHES

Dimmer switches

Like any switch, dimmers are available in either single-pole (control from one location) or three-way (control from two locations). Determine which type is required and then follow the instructions for that type switch. In the three-way application, only one dimmer is permissible. The other control must be an ordinary three-way switch.

For safety, the dimmer bracket should be grounded. If the old switch has a ground wire (normally connected to green hex head screw), fasten it to the metal box. If the box is plastic, fasten the ground wire securely to the metal dimmer bracket

NOTE: IF YOUR HOME HAS ALUMINUM WIRING, SEE INFORMATION ON PAGE 22.

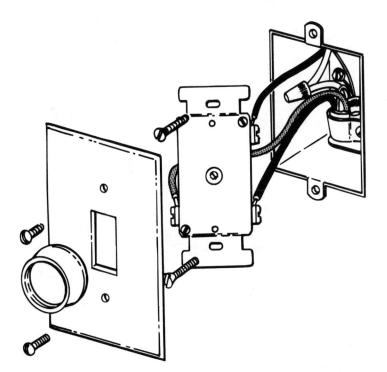

REPLACING OUTLETS

Which kind?

Many tools and appliances with metal cases come with three pronged plugs designed for use with grounded outlets. That third prong is there for an important purpose - to give you added protection from dangerous electric shock should the equipment's case come into contact with a "hot" wire. That's why you should never try to defeat that third prong's purpose (such as by using an improperly wired adapter plug). Double insulated tools have extra insulation and may also have plastic cases so that grounding is not required.

Two-slotted outlets may be replaced with the grounding type if the wall box in which the outlet mounts is grounded. It's easy to tell if it is by using a circuit tester (see p. 66). IF YOUR OUTLET BOXES ARE NOT GROUNDED AND THEY'RE IN AN AREA WHERE YOU NEED TO USE A TOOL WITH A THREE-PRONGED PLUG, CALL AN ELECTRICIAN TO MAKE THE INSTALLATION. THE SMALL COST WILL BE WELL WORTH THE EXTRA PROTECTION YOU'LL BE GETTING.

In some areas that are damp or where electrical equipment is used near water, even more protection is desirable. A device called a ground-fault circuit interrupter can provide this protection. It's designed to monitor the electricity flowing to the equipment and shut the power off almost instantly if it detects dangerous current leaving to the ground. (See p. 15.)

Some of these devices mount in the wall and do double duty as receptacles. Others replace the circuit breakers in your breaker panel. Either way, their installation is shown in this section.

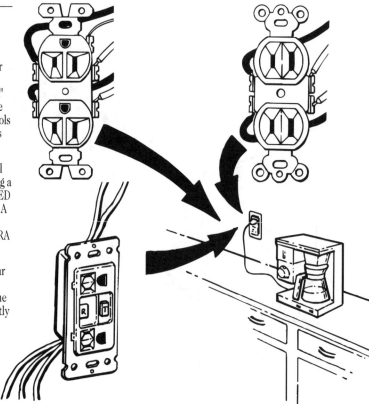

Two-wire outlets

Outlets are fast and easy to replace, as long as you pay careful attention to which color wire you attach to which terminal.

Most outlet installations have two sets of black and white wires. One set brings power in and the other set takes it out to other outlets farther down the line. The instructions here are for this type of arrangement; if you only find one set of wires attached to old outlet, just connect them to the new one according to the wire and terminal match-ups shown here.

1. REMOVE FUSE OR TURN CIRCUIT BREAKER TO OFF BEFORE WIRING. USE A CIRCUIT TESTER TO MAKE SURE EACH OF THE TWO OUTLETS IS TURNED OFF (SOMETIMES EACH IS WIRED TO A DIFFERENT CIRCUIT).

2. Remove the wall plate screw and the plate.

3. Remove the outlet mounting screws.

4. Check the old outlet to see if there is a metal link between the two outlets or if it has been broken off. If it has been broken, snap off the one on the new outlet.

5. Remove the wires from the terminal screws.

6. If necessary, strip wire insulation back 1/2 inch. Prepare as indicated on the new outlet. Reform two clockwise loops in the ends.

7. Connect the black wires to the brass terminal and the white wires to the white terminal. Tighten securely.

8. Mount outlet in box and replace cover plate.

9. Turn on power.

REPLACING OUTLETS

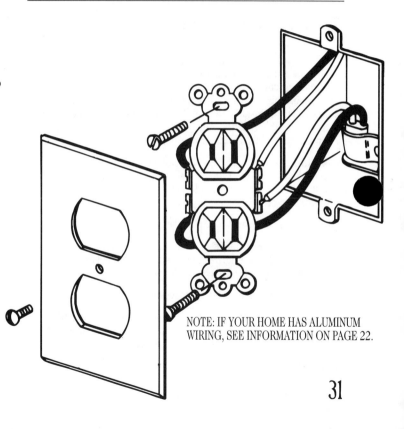

NOTE: IF YOUR HOME HAS ALUMINUM WIRING, SEE INFORMATION ON PAGE 22.

REPLACING OUTLETS

Three-wire grounding outlets

Electrical codes now require three-wire grounding outlets because of the added protection they give against the danger of electrical shock. They are simple to install and can be used to replace two-wire non-grounding outlets, PROVIDING THE BOX ITSELF IS GROUNDED. To determine this, see if a green or bare wire in the incoming cable is attached to the inside of the box. If it is, you can ground the outlet by connecting a short jumper wire between the ground wire and the green (ground) terminal on the grounding outlet, as shown here.

1. BE SURE YOU TURN OFF THE POWER BY REMOVING THE CORRECT FUSE OR TURNING THE CIRCUIT BREAKER TO OFF. Test both sides of the outlet with a neon circuit tester to be sure it has been completely disconnected.

2. Remove wall plate screw, wall plate, and outlet.

3. Check to see if break-off link has been removed. If it has, remove the same link on the new device before installing. Note and mark position and colors of wires connected to outlet being removed.

4. Unscrew terminal screws holding wires.

5. Connect green or bare wire to hex-head screw. Connect black wire to brass terminal and white wire to white terminal. Tighten securely If break-off link has been removed, reconnect as marked in 3.

6. Replace, outlet wall plate and screw.

7. Turn power back on and test outlet for power with lamp or circuit tester.

NOTE: IF YOUR HOME HAS ALUMINUM WIRING, SEE INFORMATION ON PAGE 22.

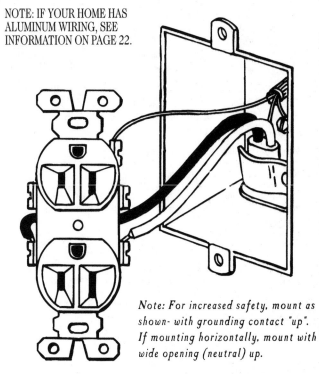

Note: For increased safety, mount as shown- with grounding contact "up". If mounting horizontally, mount with wide opening (neutral) up.

Ground trip receptacles

This is a special outlet designed to give you and your family protection from certain kinds of electrical shocks described on p. 16. It functions just like an ordinary outlet until it senses trouble, then it turns off the power.

Ground fault protection is a smart idea wherever electricity is used near water, such as a bathroom, kitchen, pool, or outdoors. It could save somebody's life. Consider making the investment.

There are two basic types of Ground Fault Receptacle, a "Feed-Thru" type and a "termination" type. The feed-thru has five wires and is connected in the branch circuit to provide not only protection to devices plugged into that receptacle, but all others further down that circuit. The termination type has only three wires and only protects the devices plugged into that receptacle. These instructions are for a "Feed-Thru" type of outlet. The only difference in installation is that you need not follow step 3 below. You should also carefully read the detailed instructions furnished with the replacement device.

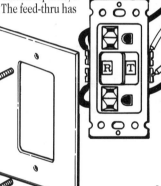

1. REMOVE FUSE OR TURN CIRCUIT BREAKER TO OFF BEFORE WIRING. USE A CIRCUIT TESTER AND TEST BOTH SIDES OF THE OLD OUTLET FOR POWER BEFORE STARTING.

2. Remove wall plate and old outlet. Disconnect all wires.

3. Determine which set of black and white wires in the box are "LINE" and which are "LOAD" Do this by connecting one set of black and

REPLACING OUTLETS

white wires to the old outlet. Cap all loose wires with tape or a wire connector. Plug a lamp into the outlet and turn it on. Restore power to the circuit by turning the circuit breaker on. If the lamp lights, you have identified the line side wires. If it doesn't, TURN OFF POWER and repeat the process with the other set of black and white wires.

4. MAKE SURE POWER IS "OFF" Connect the black line wire to the black terminal marked "LINE" on the outlet.

5. Connect the white line wire to the white terminal marked "LINE" on the outlet.

6. Group all other black wires and connect to black terminal on outlet marked "LOAD"

7. Group all other white wires and connect to white terminal on outlet marked "LOAD"

8. Connect the green or bare wire to the green hex terminal on the outlet, or connect the green hex terminal with a jumper wire to the outlet box. The box must be grounded. Check this by using a circuit tester to bridge between a black (hot) side wire and the box. If the light comes on brightly, the box is grounded.

9. Install the outlet and attach wall plate. Turn power on. The outlet is on when the reset button is pushed in.

10. To be sure that installation was correct, plug a lamp into the outlet and push test button. If the reset button pops out and the lamp stays on, you've probably wired the outlet backwards. TURN OFF POWER and recheck your work.

NOTE: IF YOUR HOME HAS ALUMINUM WIRING, SEE INFORMATION ON PAGE 22.

33

REPLACING CIRCUIT BREAKERS

BEFORE STARTING, SWITCH THE MAIN CIRCUIT BREAKER TO "OFF" OR REMOVE FUSE. DO NOT ATTEMPT TO INSTALL A NEW CIRCUIT BREAKER WITH POWER ON.

IF THERE IS NO MAIN SHUT OFF, THE JOB SHOULD BE DONE BY A LICENSED ELECTRICIAN.

Ground fault circuit interrupting (GFCI)

These are more than circuit breakers. They do everything a circuit breaker does and also give you and your family protection from certain kinds of electrical shock. GFCI breakers constantly monitor the flow of electricity through a circuit. If a leak is sensed, they shut the power off almost instantaneously. (See p. 16. for more information.)

The electrical codes require GFCI protection for bathroom, kitchen, garage, outdoor outlet and swimming pool circuits - anywhere electricity, people, and water might all come into contact at the same time. You can get the same protection on your older circuits by replacing standard breakers with GFCI breakers.

Note: A GFCI breaker needs its own private circuit. If the neutral wire is common to or shared with another circuit (see p. 81.), constant tripping may occur.

1. SWITCH THE GFCI BREAKER TO "OFF" and connect the coiled white wire furnished with the GFCI breaker to a terminal on the neutral bar of the panel. See the diagram on p. 20.

2. Connect the white neutral wire of the circuit to be protected to the breaker terminal marked "LOAD NEUTRAL." Connect the black wire of the circuit to the breaker terminal lug marked "LOAD POWER".

34

REPLACING CIRCUIT BREAKERS

3. Hold new breaker at 45° angle. Slide load end onto the load center interior hook strip and push the line side of the breaker into the "stabs" protruding from the bar seen inside the panel. The breaker should then be securely in position.

4. Replace panel front. Switch the main breaker to "ON" Then switch the new breaker to "ON". If the breaker trips, it could be from excessive leakage current. To check:

- First move handle to "OFF".

- TURN OFF MAIN CIRCUIT BREAKER and remove panel front.

- Disconnect "POWER" and "NEUTRAL" wires from breaker Replace breaker and panel front.

- Move GFCI breaker handle to "ON".

- If handle now remains in the "ON" position and trips when "TEST" is pushed, the breaker is operating properly but a there is current leaking somewhere in the circuit.

- TURN POWER OFF and try unplugging power tools, extension cords or other equipment. Go through steps 2-5 again and see if breaker works. If not, contact an electrician. If breaker remains "ON" inspect tools, lamps and appliances which have been removed to determine which caused the GFCI breaker to trip.

6. With breaker "ON" push "TEST" button. If the handle moves to "TRIP" and the power goes off on the circuit, the GFCI is operating properly. To reset, move the handle first to "OFF" and then to "ON" for normal operation.

NOTE: IF YOUR HOME HAS ALUMINUM WiRING, SEE INFORMATION ON PAGE 22.

REPLACING FIXTURES

Lighting fixtures usually come with detailed instructions on installing the hardware and on making the right electrical connections. There's nothing too difficult, just follow these instructions.

1. REMOVE FUSE OR TURN CIRCUIT BREAKER TO OFF BEFORE WIRING. MERELY SWITCHING OFF THE LIGHT AT THE WALL IS RISKY.

2. Remove the old fixture.

3. You may find three wires connected to the old fixture: a white (neutral) wire, black (hot) wire, and a green or bare wire.

4. Using twist-on wire connectors (see p. 23), connect the white and black wires on the new fixture to the white and black wires coming from the ceiling. The green wire from the fixture should be connected to the bare ground wire or to the metal box.

5. install the new fixture in the ceiling and switch on the power.

NOTE: IF YOUR HOME HAS ALUMINUM WIRING,
SEE INFORMATION ON PME 22.

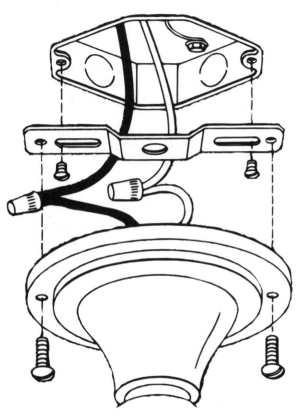

CEILING FIXTURE WIRING

ADDING ON

Working with electricity

When working with electricity, ALWAYS obey all safety rules. Electricity is dangerous if proper safeguards are not taken. All of the rules for working with electricity boil down to one caution: <u>BE CAREFUL AND DON'T WORK ON DEVICES AND APPLIANCES THAT ARE ELECTRICALLY "HOT"</u>

- ALWAYS BE SURE THE POWER IS TURNED OFF TO THE DEVICE ON WHICH YOU ARE WORKING. IF YOU ARE NOT KNOWLEDGEABLE ABOUT THE DEVICE OR APPLIANCES ON WHICH YOU ARE WORKING, DON'T TRY IT. HIRE PROFESSIONAL HELP.

- PLAN YOUR WORK AHEAD OF TIME.

- ALWAYS CHECK THE LOCAL CODES FOR YOUR OWN PROTECTION.

- NEVER REPLACE A FUSE OR CIRCUIT BREAKER WITH ONE OF A LARGER SIZE. THIS COULD CAUSE A FIRE OR DAMAGE YOUR WIRING.

- NEVER TOUCH ELECTRICAL FIXTURES WHEN YOU ARE WET OR STANDING ON A WET SURFACE.

ADDING ON

Check codes and circuit requirements

Before installing any wiring, you must check the electrical code for the community in which you reside, This is necessary, not only for your safety, but also because local codes differ from the National Electrical Code and from one location to another.

The main living area of your home requires a minimum of AWG 14 wire and a 15-amp fuse or circuit breaker. The code usually specifies how much of a load may be put on any circuit.

The kitchen, breakfast room, laundry area, and workshop have other requirements because the appliances and tools used there demand more electricity. These areas call for special purpose circuits, usually 115-volt circuits with No. 12 copper wire or No. 10 aluminum wire protected by a 20-amp fuse or circuit breaker. Again, be sure to check your local code for any special requirements.

Electric water heaters, dryers, and ranges each have their own circuit which provides the 240 volts and higher currents necessary for their operation. The size of the wire and rating of the fuse or circuit breaker will depend on the rating of the appliance under consideration.

> *Warning: Any wire added to a circuit must not be smaller than that of the circuit to which you are adding.*
> *Example: Adding #14 to a #12 circuit could result in a fire.*

Wires

Sizes and types-of wires to be used in the house are established by code and determined by location, loading and the end use, such as lighting, heating, or air conditioning.

Wires carrying electric current are analogous to pipes carrying water - the larger the pipe (wire), the more water (current) it can carry. So the more current required by the end use, the larger must be the wire.

A standard system has been established for wire sizes (gage). It's called the American Wire Gage (AWG) system. The gage number is inverse to size, that is, the larger the wire the smaller the gage number. For instance, No. 14 wire is smaller in diameter than No. 10 wire.

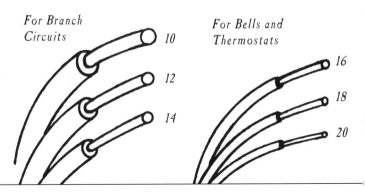

For Branch Circuits 10 12 14   *For Bells and Thermostats* 16 18 20

Solid AWG Wire Sizes (Not for Cords)

As wires increase in diameter the tendency is to make them in strands rather than solid, because larger sizes are more easily bent and otherwise handled if they are stranded rather than solid.

Wire sizes used in the home are usually AWG No. 10 to 14 and these are normally solid (single strand). To use, however, there has to be two or more wires in each cable. If you are using a No. 14 wire with two conductors, it is termed 14-2. Normally, a bare ground wire is also included. The term then becomes 14-2 with ground.

At one time, all wire used in homes was covered with a spiral armor made of steel. This is referred to as metal clad cable (TYPE MC). This type cable is rarely used in today's homes. It has been replaced by a plastic or woven jacketed cable. It's called nonmetallic cable (TYPE NMC). NMC is

ADDING ON

usually made up of two or more conductors, each with their own insulation and a ground wire which is bare. All of these are then covered with an outer skin or jacket. Wiring can also be in metal or plastic pipe called conduit. As metallic cable and conduit wiring require special techniques and tools which may be beyond the do-it yourselfer, this book will deal only with non-metallic cable installations.

> *Warning: Any wire added to a circuit must not be smaller than that of the circuit to which you are adding.*
> *Example: Adding #14 to a #12 circuit could result in a fire.*

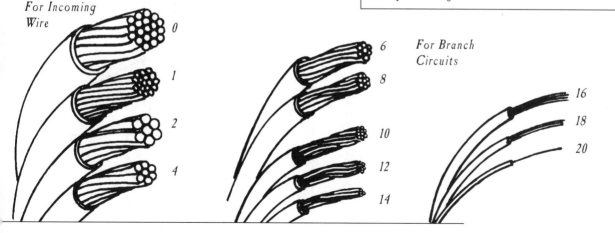

For Incoming Wire

0
1
2
4

6
8

For Branch Circuits

10
12
14

16
18
20

Stranded AWG Wire Sizes

ADDING ON

Using fish tapes

Using fish tapes makes running wiring through walls and ceilings much easier and can cut down on plaster and carpentry repairs after the job is complete. Fish tapes are long flexible metal strips and are available in several different lengths. They should have a formed hook at one or both ends. Here's how they are used:

1. After you've drilled necessary holes and cut electrical box openings, feed the fish tapes through hole "A" When the box cannot be removed, tape can also be fed through the cable opening in box.

2. Carefully twist and turn the tape until you can see it at opening "B" If tape is too short to reach hole "B', a second fish tape may be inserted through hole "B" Twist and turn tapes until they hook each other

3. Pull tape through opening "B" Securely fasten the cable to the fish tape hook.

4. Pull cable through from the opposite end and then disconnect the cable from the tape.

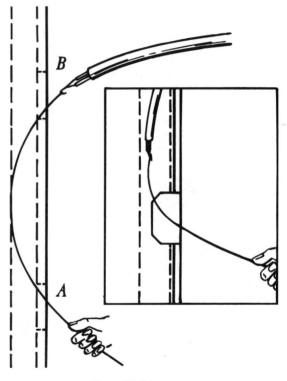

Using Fish Tape

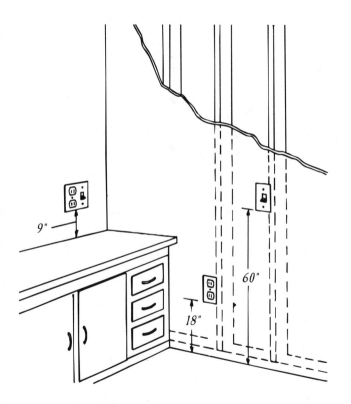

ADDING ON

Selecting location

The locations shown here are only approximate. To match, you'll want to mount any new fixture the same height as your existing ones. Try to pick a location which is both convenient to use and accessible to wire. Before making a new installation and cutting an opening for the electrical box, be sure to locate your wall studs. If you cut in the wrong place, you'll just have to repair the wall later.

ADDING ON

Mounting electrical boxes

There are different types of electrical boxes and different ways to mount them, depending on your walls. Be sure the box you buy can be used with your type of wall construction, whether it's plaster and lath or dry wall. The illustrations show typical installations you may experience. To outline the hole to be cut, use the template supplied with the box or use the box to trace a cutting outline on the wall. Drill starter holes, cut around the outline with a key hole saw, then discard cutout.

CUTTING A HOLE FOR AN ELECTRICAL BOX

D) BOX FITS DRY WALL OR PANEL AWAY FROM ANY STUDS.

A) CEILING TYPE APPLICATIONS REQUIRE DEVICE FOR CLAMPING TO JOISTS.

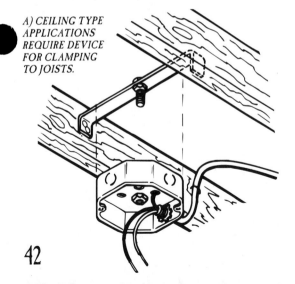

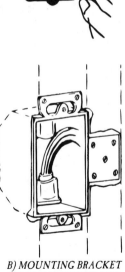

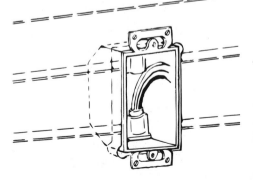

C) BOX DESIGNED FOR INSTALLATION IN WOOD LATH AND PLASTER WALL

B) MOUNTING BRACKET ON BOX DESIGNED FOR FASTENING TO STUD.

42

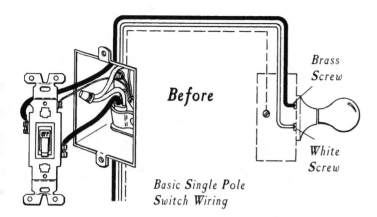

Brass
Screw

Before

White
Screw

*Basic Single Pole
Switch Wiring*

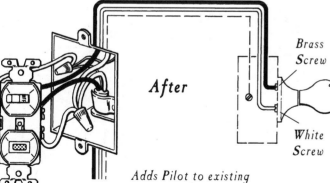

Brass
Screw

After

White
Screw

*Adds Pilot to existing
switch and Light.
Neutral Required*

ADDING ON

Combination devices

Adding a device can be almost as easy as replacing a switch if you can use combination devices. These handy electrical units are available in combinations of switches, pilot ; lights, and outlets. You can buy a combined switch and pilot, or outlet and switch, or two switches on one mounting strap. They're shaped like a double outlet and use a wall plate which fits a double outlet.

Combination devices give you the flexibility you may need in one convenient device. For example, if you need to add a new switch and light rather than install a new box, it may be easier to run a wire from the light to the existing switch box, and install a combination device with two switches. (See p. 43.)

Shown are typical installations you may be considering. In planning your particular installation, check to be sure a neutral wire is available if it is required. In some installations of switches and lights, the power is taken directly to the light (see p. 84) and the neutral wire is not present in the switch box.

NOTE: IF YOUR HOME HAS ALUMINUM WIRING, SEE INFORMATION ON PAGE 22.

ADDING ON

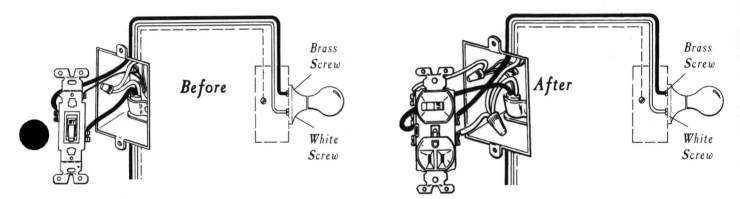

Before

Brass Screw

White Screw

Basic Single Pole Switch Wiring

After

Brass Screw

White Screw

Adds Outlet to existing switch and Light, Neutral Required

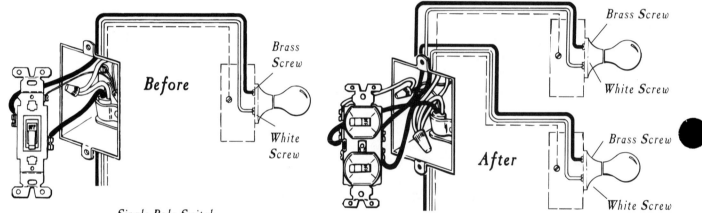

Before

Brass
Screw

White
Screw

Single Pole Switch

After

Brass Screw

White Screw

Brass Screw

White Screw

*Adds Switch for new light in existing
switch box, Neutral Required*

ADDING ON

Extending a circuit

In adding on, you have to run wire from the power source usually an existing outlet, to the new location. It can go through a wall, an attic or a basement, or behind a baseboard.

If you are installing a ceiling fixture, or extending power along the somewhat or to an adjacent or opposite wall,running wire through the attic or basement is probably your best bet, especially if the joists are exposed and this area is accessible.

Extending wire along the wall behind the baseboard is an alternate to also consider. If there is a door in the way, choose a different method, such as running the wire through the basement, ceiling or attic.

Wiring through a wall works best when the new fixture is in line with the existing power source. if wall studs obstruct your wiring, you may want to choose another method.

Details on extending a circuit are shown on this and following pages.

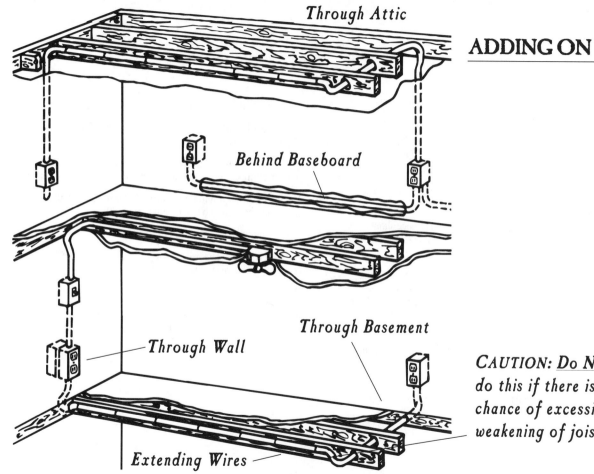

Through Attic

Behind Baseboard

Through Basement

Through Wall

Extending Wires

CAUTION: <u>Do Not</u> do this if there is chance of excessive weakening of joist.

47

ADDING ON

Wire extension through a wall

Sometimes you may have to bring a wire into another room by going through a wall. These instructions tell you how.

1. BEFORE YOU DO ANYTHING, REMOVE FUSE OR SWITCH OFF CIRCUIT BREAKER CONTROLLING THE CIRCUIT YOU'RE WORKING ON.

2. To extend power from source A to new outlet B. remove cover plate and outlet from source A to get to the electrical box.

3. Inside the box are "knockouts". The knockout you remove should face the direction you're extending the wire - in this case, toward the wall. So use a screwdriver to punch out the rear knockout.

4. Next, pinpoint the new fixture location by finding wall studs, either by knocking on the wall or using a magnetic stud finder. Location is determined by how the electrical box is attached. You probably don't have enough depth to mount the new box back-to-back with the old box so it should be offset slightly.

5. Put your new electrical box against the wall or use template supplied with box where you want it, and draw an outline on the wall. See box mounting instructions on p. 42.

6. Drill starter holes, cut around the outline with a keyhole saw, then discard the cutout.

7. Take off six inches of outside insulation from one end of cable.

8. Feed cable through the knockout of Box A out wall opening at B. Tighten cable clamp at Box A.

9. At the new opening, strip about 1/2 inch of insulation from wires and put wires through knockout of the new box. Tighten cable clamp.

10. Match new wires at A to source wires (black to black, white to white, and bare ground to bare ground) (p. 80).

11. Replace outlet, cover plate, and screw.

12. Connect wires B (black wire to brass terminal, white wire to white terminal, and bare ground to green hex head screw).

13. Replace outlet, cover plate, and screw.

14. Turn the power back on and use a neon circuit tester or lamp to see if the wire extension is working correctly.

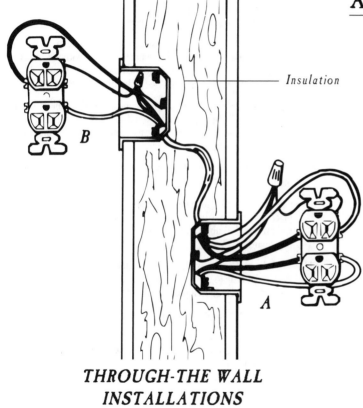

Insulation

B

A

THROUGH-THE WALL
INSTALLATIONS

ADDING ON

Wire extension behind baseboards

Use these instructions to extend a wire in the same room, such as when you're adding an outlet or switch.

1. BEFORE STARTING, SWITCH CIRCUIT BREAKER TO"OFF" OR REMOVE FUSE. CHECK WITH A NEON CIRCUIT TESTER TO MAKE SURE THE POWER IS OFF.

2. To extend power from source A to point B. remove cover plate and outlet from source A to get to the electrical box.

3. Inside the box are "knockouts" Remove the one facing the direction you're extending the wire - in this case, toward the floor. Use a screwdriver to punch out the bottom knockout.

4. Next, pinpoint the new outlet's location by finding wall studs, either by knocking on the wall or using a magnetic/electronic stud finder. Location is determined by the type of box and how it's attached. See p. 42 for information on box installation.

5. Put your new electrical box against the wall where you want it, and draw an outline on the wall or use the template supplied with the box. (If you have lath and plaster, leave enough lath at top and bottom to attach the box.) Drill starter holes, cut around the outline with a keyhole saw. then discard the cutout.

6. Measure the distance from source to new fixture along baseboard. Take off the baseboard between those points. Drill a hole in the wall below A and B and behind the baseboard.

7. Cut out a groove in the wall and studs - be sure it's deep enough for a piece of 1/2 inch EMT (electrical metallic tubing) with 5/8" outer diameter, to comfortably fit behind the baseboard. Choose cable-size according to circuit amperage. See p. 36 for more information.

8. Take off six inches of insulation from one end of the cable. Using fish tape, feed cable through the hole you drilled below source A, and through the knockout of Box A. Leave a minimum of six inches of cable for connection.

9. Cut enough cable to reach the new outlet (with a minimum of six inches for connections). Remove six inches of cable insulation.

10. Cut a piece of EMT long enough to span the studs and fasten it in place. Lay the EMT into the groove behind the baseboard. The EMT will protect the cable from nail damage when reinstalling the baseboard.

11. Feed the cable through the EMT and then through the hole below new outlet B up to the opening you cut and through the box knockout. Then tighten the cable clamp.

12. Fasten the new electrical box to the wall.

13. Strip about 1/2 inch of insulation from the ends of wires at the electrical box and connect them to the new outlet. (See p. 79 for instructions.)

14. Put outlet in box and install mounting screws and cover plate screw.

15. Strip about 1/2 inch of insulation from wires at power source A.

16. At A match new wires to source wires (black to black, white to white, bare ground to bare ground).

17. Replace outlet, cover plate and screws.

18. Turn the power back on. Using a neon circuit tester or lamp, check if the wire extension is working properly.

19. Replace baseboard.

ADDING ON

> *NOTE:* Cutting notches or drilling holes in studs or joists may cause structural damage.

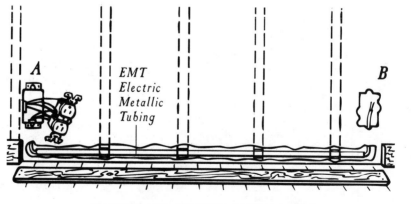

EMT
Electric
Metallic
Tubing

BASEBOARD CIRCUIT INSTALLATION

51

ADDING ON

Wire extension through an attic or basement

Read all instructions before you begin.

Where the joists are exposed, running a circuit extension through on attic or basement requires the same basic steps.

Use whatever route is most convenient. The instructions below use on attic extension as an example; a basement extension could be made with only minor adaptation.

1. BEFORE STARTING, SWITCH CIRCUIT BREAKER TO "OFF" OR REMOVE FUSE; CHECK WITH A NEON CIRCUIT TESTER TO MAKE SURE THE POWER IS OFF.

2. To extend power from source A to new outlet B, remove cover plate and outlet at A to get to the electrical box.

3. Inside the box are "knockouts". The knockout you remove should face in the direction you are extending the wire. Use a screwdriver to punch out the knockout.

4. Next, pinpoint the new outlet's location by finding the wall studs, either by knocking on the wall or by using a magnetic/electronic stud finder. The distance from the stud is determined by the type of box and how it is to be attached. (For lath and plaster walls, drill a hole in the center of the location. Keep making it bigger until you locate lath. Locate hole as shown on page 40.)

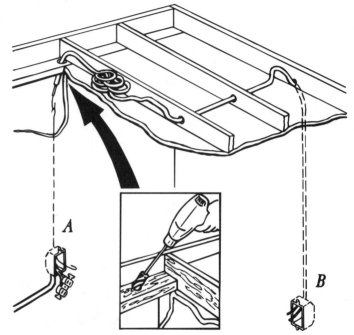

Drilling Holes Through The Ceiling

Ceiling or Attic Installation

52

ADDING ON

5. From the attic, directly above A and above new outlet B, drill holes large enough to clear the cable. Also drill joists where cable will pass through. To avoid obstructions, you may need to drill at an angle.

6. Remove six inches of outside insulation from one end of the cable. Using fish tape, feed the cable through the hole you drilled above A. Pull cable out through box at A and remove fish tape. Leave 6-8 inches of wire extending out of the box for connections.

7. Again, use fish tape, pull cable through the hole above B down and out the opening. Pull the excess cable through the hole, then cut the cable, allowing enough wire to enter the box and extend out a minimum of 6 inches.

8. Strip wires, put cable through box knockout and tighten cable clamp to secure cable.

9. Fasten the new box to the wall.

10. Strip about 1/2 inch of insulation from the ends of wires at the electrical box and connect them to the new outlet. (See p. 79 for instructions.)

11. Mount outlet to the box and install the cover plate and screw.

12. Strip about 1/2 inch of insulation from wires at A. Match and connect new wires to source wires (black to black, white to white, bare ground to bare ground).

13. Replace outlet, cover plate, and screws.

14. Turn the power back on and check both outlets with a neon circuit tester on lamp to see if they are working properly.

ADDING ON

Adding a circuit

Sometimes you'll find that your need for more electrical power has expanded beyond the point where it can be safely accommodated by your existing wiring. If this happens, you may need to install a new circuit. Follow the wiring instructions in "adding on" for running wires to and through the area needing the added capability. To energize the circuit, you should be able to make a connection to your main panel box by adding a new circuit breaker or using a spare fuse socket. If neither of these are possible, then a sub-panel must be added.

In either case be sure your panel box has a main disconnect, one that controls all circuits contained in the box. IF THERE IS NO MAIN SHUTOFF, DO NOT ATTEMPT THE WORK. CALL AN ELECTRICIAN. When installing a circuit breaker, make sure the one you have is compatible with and will fit your panel. Manufacturers use different mountings and they may not be interchangeable. Before buying a circuit breaker, take note of the panel make and model or bring a sample to the store. After you have completely wired your new circuit, it is time to connect the new circuit to the main panel.

1. TURN THE MAIN BREAKER OR SWITCH TO "OFF" OR REMOVE MAIN FUSE PULL OUT. BE CAREFUL! REMEMBER, THE INCOMING POWER CABLE MAY STILL BE LIVE EVEN THOUGH THE REST OF THE BOX HAS BEEN DISCONNECTED.

2. Remove front trim from panel.

3. Select and remove appropriate knockout through which the cable will enter the panel. Install cable clamp in the knockout. Feed the wire through the clamp and into the panel. Tighten cable clamp.

4. Route the cable around the perimeter of box to the point where the connections will be made. Connect the black wire to the fuse socket or circuit breaker, the white wire to neutral bar and the bare ground wire to the ground terminal strip.

5. Turn the circuit breaker to "off" and install it in the panel. Remove appropriate punch out in front trim to clear new circuit breaker or fuse and reinstall trim.

6. Turn the main power on, then energize new circuit by turning on the breaker or installing the fuse. Then use your neon circuit tester to be sure circuit is working properly. Note: If new fuse blows or circuit breaker trips, do not attempt to re-energize the circuit until the condition causing the tripping or blowing is corrected. (See "Troubleshooting, p. 73).

Adding a sub panel

The cable which feeds your sub panel should match the ampere capacity of the new panel. To determine what amperage you need, refer to the panel rating and the manufacturer's instructions included with the sub panel. Also check your local Code and see p. 19. Also be sure that the sub panel you buy has sufficient capacity for the number of circuits you wish to connect to it. Installing a sub panel requires use of two circuits in the main panel. Be certain your new sub panel can accommodate these two circuits plus your additions.

IF THERE IS NO MAIN SHUTOFF, DO NOT ATTEMPT THE WORK. CALL AN ELECTRICIAN.

1. BEFORE STARTING, SWITCH THE MAIN CIRCUIT BREAKER TO "OFF" OR REMOVE MAIN FUSE. BE CAREFUL! REMEMBER THE INCOMING POWER CABLE AND BREAKERS ARE STILL LIVE EVEN THOUGH THE REST OF THE BOX HAS BEEN DISCONNECTED.

2. The sub panel is usually mounted next to your main panel and connected with a conduit nipple.

3. Run your extension cable from the main panel to the sub panel through the conduit nipple. Make sure that there is extra cable at each end to make the actual connections.

4. Cut the insulated wires long enough to connect to the screw terminals, neutral bar and equipment ground bar.

5. The black and red wires connect to the screw terminal at the top of your new panel, the white wire connects to the neutral bar, and the green or bare wire connects to the equipment ground bar.

ADDING ON

6. Cut the wires within the main panel long enough to connect to the branch breaker terminals, the neutral, and the equipment ground bars of the main panel.

7. The black and red wires are connected to the branch breaker terminals, the white wire is connected to the neutral bar, and the green or bare wire is connected to the equipment ground bar (See illus.)

8. You are now ready to add branch circuits to your sub panel. To add circuits follow the instructions on p. 52.

MAIN PANEL   *SUB PANEL*

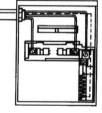
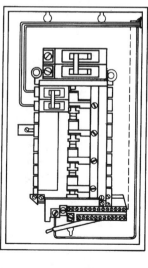

Use 3/4" conduit nipple (or Larger), 4 Lock nuts and 2 bushings

55

OUTDOOR WIRING

Electricity needn't be confined to indoors. With some special devices and wiring, you can have electricity perform many jobs outside your home, such as lighting your yard and walkways, powering tools, and even helping you light a charcoal fire and turn a rotisserie.

Just remember that because outdoor wiring is exposed to rain, snow, dirt and wide ranges of temperature, some special materials and procedures have to be used to give your installation safety and reliability.

Installing outdoor outlets

The National Electrical Code now requires ground fault protection by breaker or outlet on any outdoor outlet. This automatically shuts off power if a dangerous leakage of electrical current known as a ground fault is detected. See p. 17. Outlets called Ground Trip Receptacles (GTR's) provide this protection, as do Ground Fault Circuit Interrupting (GFCI) breakers, which install in the panel box and give protection over the entire circuit. To wire a GTR receptacle, follow the instructions given on p. 30 for wiring the device. Or if you install a Ground Fault Circuit Interrupting (GFCI) breaker in the panel box, follow the instructions on p. 34, and use a standard three-wire grounding outlet with a weatherproof cover. It's easiest if you can choose a location for your outdoor outlet that's both convenient and near an inside source of power A location on an outside wall opposite an outlet or an inside wall is ideal.

One other source is a ceiling junction box in the basement. If no power source is available, a new circuit from your main panel may be needed.

1. TURN CIRCUIT BREAKER TO OFF" OR REMOVE FUSE. TEST WITH NEON CIRCUIT TESTER TO BE SURE ALL CIRCUITS SUPPLYING THE OUTLET HAVE BEEN DISCONNECTED.

2. Mark and cut hole in wall. Position box so it's not back to back with inside outlet.

3. Install cable from box A through hole at B. Cut and remove six inches of jacket and feed through the cable clamp of box B.

4. Mount box B.

5. Connect outlet at B. Connect black wire to brass terminal, white wire to white terminal and ground wire to the metal box and the ground terminal of the outlet.

6. Install outlet and weatherproof plate.

7. Connect inside wires to outlet as in 5 above.

8. Turn on power and test new outlet with neon circuit tester and trip button, if GFCI, with tester plugged to verify proper GFCI wiring.

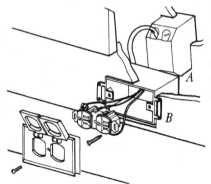

Note: If outlet is to be used for anything other than temporary. (Dry weather job). use GE 9232- DHD or GE 9233-GHD weatherproof covers.

56

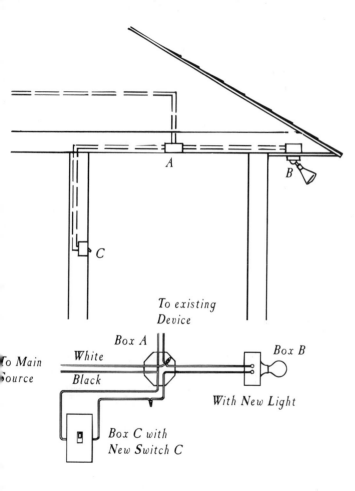

OUTDOOR LIGHTING

Outdoor lighting can be a great convenience for many homes, as well as serving to highlight the house, gardens and landscaping for dramatic nighttime effects.

Outdoor lighting can be installed as spotlights under the eaves, as a post lantern or in the form of garden lighting. Instructions are given here for eaves and post lantern lighting. Installing garden lighting is similar to installing post lighting. Also, low-voltage kits for garden lighting are available.

Don't forget that not only should there be a source of power near the location you choose but you'll also need to run a wire from the fixture to a conveniently located switch. Finally make sure your outdoor installations include only outdoor-type lighting fixtures and bulbs.

Under-eaves installations

1. TURN OFF POWER BY REMOVING FUSE OR SWITCHING CIRCUIT TO "OFF." TEST FOR POWER WITH NEON CIRCUIT TESTER.

2. Locate and expose power source, such as a ceiling light or attic junction box A.

3. Install cable from junction box to new box location and install box B.

4. Run cable from the power source to the switch location C.

5. Mount devices, wiring per diagram. Box could be a weatherproof surface-mounted type where the fixture or lights mount to it, with a weatherproof cover.

6. Turn on power and test.

57

OUTDOOR WIRING

Installing post lanterns

1. TURN YOUR MAIN POWER PANEL TO "OFF" Check to see if you have any outlet or junction box in the basement near the side of your house towards your new installation. If so, you should be able to connect the wiring for the post lantern to this junction box and the indoor circuit, assuming a 15 or 20 amp circuit being utilized can handle the increased load. If there is no wiring handy, you'll have to run a circuit from the nearest available location or run a new circuit from your main panel. See p. 54.

2. Drill a hole the size of your conduit through the wood sill plate right above your foundation.

3. To protect the wire, run plastic (PVC) conduit through the hole to the outside and down the wall extending underground.

4. Pull underground type UF cable through conduit to the outside, run underground, and bury it 12" to 18" below the surface If rocks are present, pour sand around the cable for protection before filling in the trench. A board buried just over the cable will help protect it from shovel damage should someone start digging nearby.

5. Run the UF cable up through the post to lantern B as indicated in the manufacturer's instructions.

6. Connect white to white, black to black and ground to ground at lantern.

7. Run wire from junction box in basement A through wall to switch box C. Connections as shown in diagram on p.57.

8. Turn on power and test for proper operation.

9. Similar wiring with or without the switch can be used for post-mounted outdoor outlets. Be certain such outlets have ground fault protection.

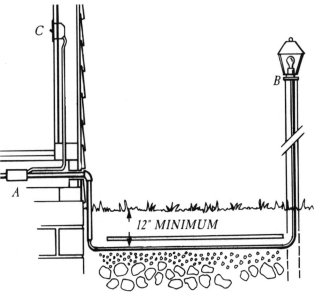

CORDS, PLUGS, FEED-THROUGH SWITCHES AND LAMPS

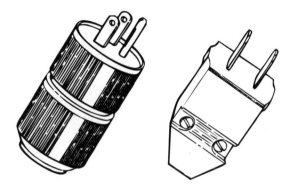

There are several types of replaceable plugs and connectors. All plugs now being produced and many of the older ones are of the dead front type which means that they have no exposed wires or live screws after assembly. Connectors have always been dead front.

Tips on care

Properly cared for extension and appliance cords will give long and faithful service. Extension cords and appliance cords should be regularly inspected for damage. Damaged cords should be immediately repaired or replaced. If the plug doesn't seem to fit an outlet properly, check the outlet with another plug to be sure that the outlet contacts have not lost their spring. Do not adjust plug blades unless they are obviously deformed.

Some other tips for proper use and care are:

• ALWAYS GRASP PLUG WHEN DISCONNECTING CORD NEVER PULL ON THE CORD ITSELF.

• WHEN DISCONNECTING APPLIANCE CORDS, ALWAYS DISCONNECT AT THE OUTLET FIRST, THEN AT THE APPLIANCE.

• ALWAYS ROUTE EXTENSION CORDS SO THEY ARE FREE FROM POSSIBLE DAMAGE. DO NOT RUN THEM THROUGH DOORWAYS OR UNDER RUGS.

• DO NOT EXCEED THE RATED CAPACITY OF EXTENSION CORDS.

• TO PREVENT DAMAGE, UNPLUG, COIL AND STORE CORDS WHEN NOT IN USE.

This section will show you how to replace plugs, whether on extension cords or appliance cords and whether they have two or three prongs.

59

CORDS, PLUGS, FEED-THROUGH SWITCHES AND LAMPS

Cord inspection

All cords, especially those used on appliances, tools and clocks, should be inspected on a regular basis. Look for damage to the cord where it leaves the plug, connector or appliance. Inspect also for damaged areas along the cord.

On grounding-type extension cords, the continuity of the ground circuit should be checked using a continuity tester (p. 68) as shown here.

With two wire cords, connection color matching is not important unless the plug is polarized. In that case, one blade will be wider than the other Connectors can also be polarized by having one slot wider than the other. In two-conductor cords that have an outer insulation, the individual covering for each conductor is black or white. For correct connections, the white wire is attached to the silver colored screw and the black one to the brass screw On flat parallel cord, the conductor with a rib is the white conductor.

In three-conductor cords, the third conductor is green. In this case, the black wire is fastened to the brass screw and the white wire to the silver screw. The green wire is attached to the grounding screw. On flat parallel cord, the conductor with a rib is the white conductor.

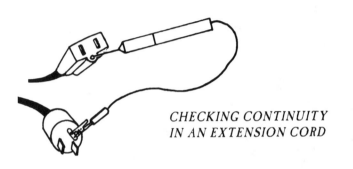

CHECKING CONTINUITY IN AN EXTENSION CORD

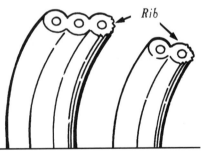

Rib

Two & Three Wire Cords

60

CORDS, PLUGS, FEED-THROUGH SWITCHES AND LAMPS

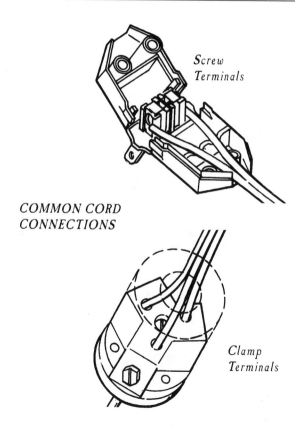

Screw Terminals

COMMON CORD CONNECTIONS

Clamp Terminals

Replacing plugs and connectors

1. BEFORE STARTING, BE SURE THE CORD IS NOT PLUGGED INTO A POWER SOURCE. Remove the old device by cutting the cord where it leaves the plug or connector. This is an area of high wear and the wire may be damaged at this point.

2. Prepare wire as indicated on the instructions provided with the replacement device. Typical connections used are screw terminals insulation piercing clamp terminals.

3. On devices with screw on clamp terminals, the strands of each conductor should be twisted together. DO NOT tin or solder the twisted strands.

4. ON DEVICES OF THE INSULATION PIERCING TYPE, THE INDIVIDUAL CONDUCTORS MUST NOT BE STRIPPED.

CORDS, PLUGS, FEED-THROUGH SWITCHES AND LAMPS

Strain relief

All plugs and connectors provide a means of strain relief. This prevents a pull on the wire being transmitted directly to the terminal connection. Strain relief means used are:

1. Capture of the wire by the closure of parts of the plug or connector.

2. The use of a strain relief knot internal to the plus or connector. (Generally used in two-wire cord only.)

3. Separate cable clamps.

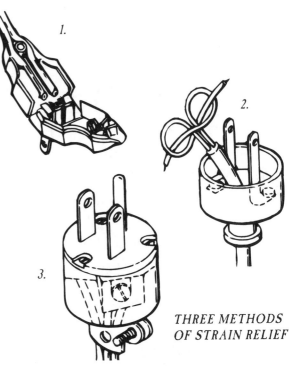

Plugs 2 & 3 are not UL Listed and are not recommended by GE

THREE METHODS OF STRAIN RELIEF

CORDS, PLUGS, FEED-THROUGH SWITCHES AND LAMPS

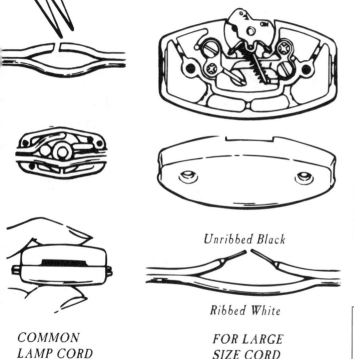

COMMON LAMP CORD

Unribbed Black

Ribbed White

FOR LARGE SIZE CORD

Adding feed-through cord switch

Cord switches are inexpensive, easy-to-install devices that are ideal for controlling the operation of a single electrical appliance. For example, you may have a small table radio with a broken switch. With a feed-through switch, you'd be able to add another "on-off" control point in the cord. Or you might have a power tool you use in a place with a hard-to-reach outlet. Install a feed-through switch in the cord and you can control it from an easy-to-reach point.

To install a feed-through cord switch, you need only separate the conductors of the cord and cut one, the black or unribbed one (first be sure the cord isn't plugged in). Then open the switch housing (usually by removing screws) and insert the cord in the appropriate slots. Be sure to follow the exact instruction that comes with the switch. Most commonly a pair of sharp contacts will pierce the severed cord while the uncut cord passes through a smooth channel. Screw terminals may also be used. Screw the switch back together and it's ready to serve.

> *Note: The GE switch will not accept much of the cord sizes/types viewed used with power tools.*

REWIRING LAMPS

Today's homes have many forms of lighting fixtures. Some are mounted permanently in your walls and ceilings, others are portable table and floor lamps. For a discussion of wall or ceiling fixtures see p. 36.

Portable lamps

The vulnerable electrical parts of portable lamps are the bulb, the socket and switch assembly, and the cord and plug. If the lamp will not light, or if it flickers, be sure there is nothing wrong with the power to the outlet, that the plug is fully inserted in the outlet, and that the bulb is good. If none of these seems to be the problem, the socket or the cord needs to be replaced.

Remove the plug from the outlet. Remove the shade from the lamp. Disassemble lamp socket. Looking at the cord may tell you that it's causing the malfunctions. Check by attaching alligator clip of the battery continuity tester to the brass screw on the lamp socket. Then touch the tester to the plug prongs. One of the prongs should cause the tester to glow. Repeat the test with other plug prong and the alligator clip connected to the white screw. If both tests cause the tester to glow, the problem is in the socket.

To check the socket, attach the tester's alligator clip to the brass screw on the side of the socket. Touch the other lead to the contact in the center of the socket and operate the switch. The tester should go on and off. If there is no light or if the tester does not go on and off, the socket is defective and should be replaced. This is a good time to replace cord to reduce future trouble.

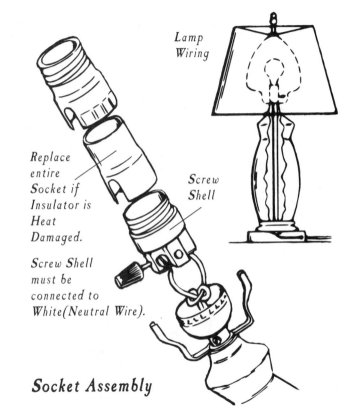

Lamp Wiring

Replace entire Socket if Insulator is Heat Damaged.

Screw Shell

Screw Shell must be connected to White(Neutral Wire).

Socket Assembly

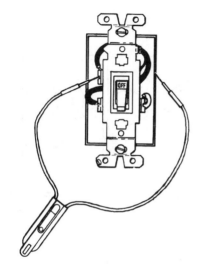

TROUBLESHOOTING

Using a neon voltage tester

Checking for power at switch

CAREFULLY REMOVE THE WALL PLATE. Touch one lead of the neon circuit tester to the metal box in the wall and then touch the other lead to each of the terminals on the switch. (If the switch has push-in terminals, this check cannot be made.) If the box is plastic, the test must be made between the switch terminal and the ground wire. The tester should glow if there is power coming to the switch. USE CAUTION, CIRCUIT IS LIVE.

There is a good chance that there is no neutral- if plastic box has no ground wire and there is no neutral, there may be a problem testing.

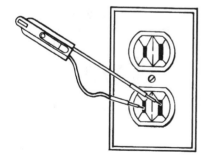

Checking for power at outlet

Insert tester leads into hot (narrow slot) and neutral slots. Tester will glow if circuit is live. Make sure tester prods are thin enough to make contact with outlet contacts.

65

TROUBLESHOOTING

Checking for grounded box with two-wire outlets

Insert one lead into hot (narrow) slot and touch the other lead to bare metal wall plate or to metal mounting screw. Tester will glow if box is properly grounded. Important tester must glow as brightly on ground test as it glows when put across two slots of outlet. If it does not, the box is not grounded.

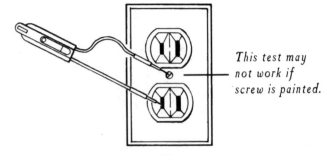

This test may not work if screw is painted.

Checking for ground on grounding outlets

Insert one lead into the hot (narrow) slot and the other lead into the U-shaped ground slot. Tester will glow if grounding slot is properly grounded. Important: tester must glow as brightly on ground test as it glows when put across two slots of outlet. If it does not, box is not grounded.

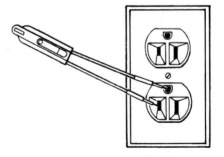

66

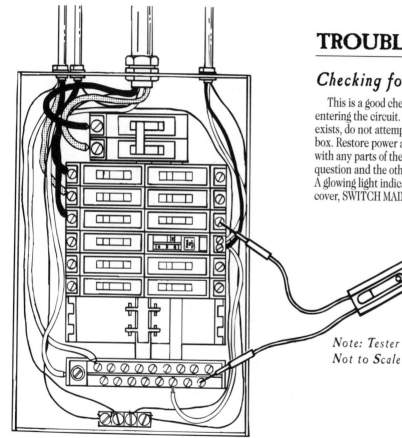

TROUBLESHOOTING

Checking for power at a panel box

This is a good check to be sure a breaker is working and that power is entering the circuit. TURN MAIN BREAKER "OFF" If no main shut-off exists, do not attempt this test. With all power off, remove front of panel box. Restore power and, taking care not to let your body come in contact with any parts of the box, touch one lead to the terminal by the breaker in question and the other lead to the neutral strip at the bottom of the box. A glowing light indicates power in this part of the circuit. Before replacing cover, SWITCH MAIN BREAKER TO "OFF"

Note: Tester
Not to Scale

67

TROUBLESHOOTING

Using a continuity tester

Testing a fuse

CAUTION: USE CONTINUITY TESTERS ONLY WITH DISCONNECTED DEVICES. To check a plug-type fuse, touch one lead to the contact point on the base of the fuse and the other lead to the metal spring contact on Type "S" fuses (illustrated) or the metal threads of Edison-base fuses. If the tester lights, the fuse is good.

Cartridge fuses are checked similarly. Touch one lead to one end and the other lead to the other end. A glowing light means the fuse is good.

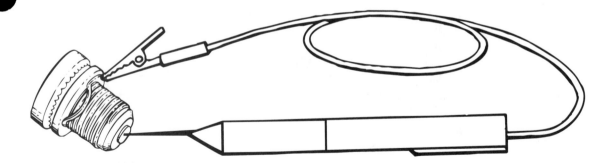

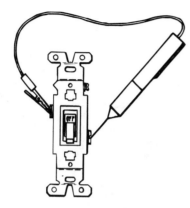

TROUBLESHOOTING

Using a continuity tester

Testing a single-pole switch

CAUTION: USE CONTINUITY TESTERS ONLY WITH DISCONNECTED DEVICES. Attach the alligator clip lead to one of the line terminals. Fasten the other lead to the other line terminal and operate switch. The switch, if operating properly, will cause the tester to light when the switch is in the "ON" position and shut off when the switch is in the "OFF" position. There should be no continuity (shown by a glowing light) between either terminal and bracket.

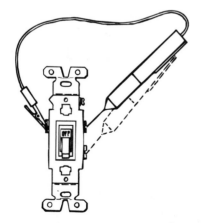

Testing three-way switches

CAUTION: USE CONTINUITY TESTERS ONLY WITH DISCONNECTED DEVICES. Attach the alligator clip to the terminal marked "COMMON" or with a different colored screw. Touch the other lead to one of the other two line terminals and operate the switch. The tester should only light when touched to one of the terminals. Then move the switch handle to its other position. Now the light should glow when the tester is touched to the terminal that originally caused no lighting. There should be no continuity (shown by a glowing light) between either terminal and bracket.

69

TROUBLESHOOTING

Using a continuity tester

Testing four-way switches

CAUTION: USE CONTINUITY TESTERS ONLY WITH DISCONNECTED DEVICES. These switches work in the middle of a circuit between two three-way switches (see p. 86).

Connect alligator clip to terminal " 1 " Touch the other lead to other three line terminals. The light should glow at only one of them. If it glows at, say, terminal "3", it should also glow when connected between "2" and "4" Then flip the switch. Now you should get a glow between " 1 " and "2" and between "3" and "4".

Finally, connect the alligator clip to the metal mounting strap. Touch the other lead to each of the terminals and operate the switch handle up and down. The tester now should not light in any position.

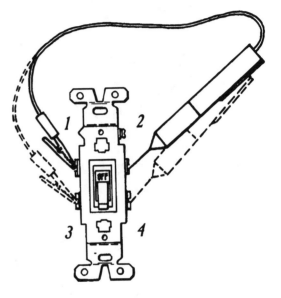

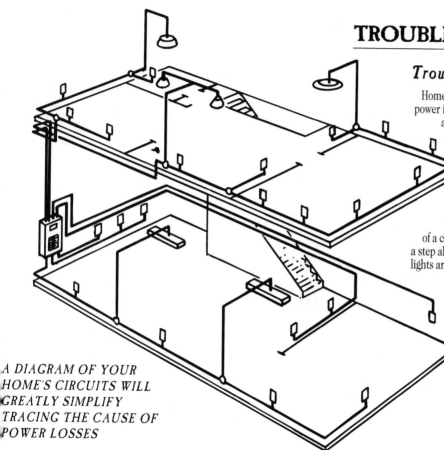

TROUBLESHOOTING

Troubleshooting power losses

Home power failures can involve anything from losing power in the whole house to losing it in just one lamp or appliance. In the more extensive losses - those where many circuits are out - call your utility or electrical contractor for help. These failures probably involve the main power panel or some part of the wiring lending to it, and require more expertise than is given or intended in this book.

Problems in just one circuit or some part or parts of a circuit can usually be solved by homeowners. You are a step ahead if you have already identified when outlets and lights are in each circuit. See p. 20.

A DIAGRAM OF YOUR HOME'S CIRCUITS WILL GREATLY SIMPLIFY TRACING THE CAUSE OF POWER LOSSES

TROUBLESHOOTING

Power losses-when circuit breakers aren't tripped or fuses not blown, and there is no power on any part of the circuit

First, check to be sure that circuit breakers or fuse sockets are good. Use a neon test light to check for electricity leaving the fuse or circuit breaker feeding the brunch circuit as shown on p. 67. If you do not get a light with the breaker "ON" or a good fuse in place, the trouble is in the panel and the problem should be referred to a qualified electrician. If this check shows power going to the branch circuit the problem is probably in the branch circuit.

The problem probably lies in the wiring between the main panel box and a junction box, ceiling box, outlet on the dead circuit or at a connection point. To check FIRST REMOVE FUSE OR TURN CIRCUIT BREAKER TO "OFF" Then open each junction box, ceiling box and outlet,

checking for wires that may have come loose from their connections. Make sure any twist-on connectors are tight. Look for broken wires especially near or at connection points.

If you can't find the problem with the above checks, and there is still no electricity at the first connection, box or outlet, the problem is probably a broken wire. The wire could have been damaged during installation with a misplaced staple or one that was driven too hard. Check exposed portion of the wiring to see if you can spot the damage. If the wiring is concealed, you may want to refer the problem to a qualified electrician.

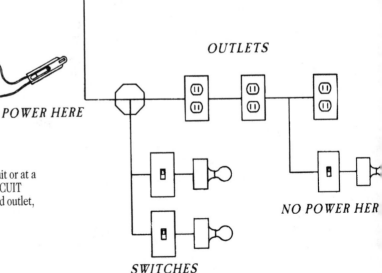

JUNCTION BOX

PANEL BOX

POWER HERE

OUTLETS

SWITCHES

NO POWER HERE

TROUBLESHOOTING

Power losses- when circuit breaker is tripped or fuses blown

Such losses are almost always caused by an overload or by a short circuit. If you have fuses, you can sometimes tell what caused the failure by looking at the blown fuse. An overload causes the metal strip in the fuse to melt slowly. But a short circuit causes such a fast melt that the window usually becomes discolored. A circuit breaker which trips immediately upon reset is probably indicative of a short circuit.

Overloads

Overloads may be caused by too many appliances or tools on one circuit. That new electric saw may have been a little too much for that particular circuit to bear. Try plugging it in somewhere else. Do not put in a higher rated circuit breaker or fuse (15 or 20 amps in your general circuits, 20 amps in kitchen or laundry circuits and 25 or 30 amps in special circuits serving one large load such as a water heater). See p. 38. You might need to have additional circuits added to your main panel box to accommodate all your new appliances or tools.

Many parts of the country use only 20 AMP Receptacle Circuits

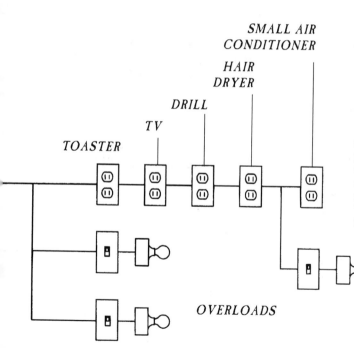

SMALL AIR
CONDITIONER

HAIR
DRYER

DRILL

TV

TOASTER

OVERLOADS

TROUBLESHOOTING

Short circuits

If a short circuit caused the problem, it may be in the circuit itself or, more likely, in an appliance plugged into the circuit. To find the problem, first check any appliances or lamps that, when turned on and plugged in cause the power to go off. If the circuit trips when turning on a light switch, the problem may be in the light fixture. If you can't find any clues to an offending appliance or lamp, a step-by-step check of the circuit is necessary.

Before undertaking a circuit analysis, unplug every device plugged into the circuit in question. Then, following the instructions given below, disconnect parts of the circuit and turn the power back on to the rest of the circuit. Junction boxes or outlets can be used to disconnect the different circuit parts. When you can turn the power back on and it remains on, the disconnected part of the circuit contains the short.

1. Turn off all lights and appliances on the circuit. Pull plugs wherever you can.

2. REMOVE THE FUSE OR TURN THE CIRCUIT BREAKER TO "OFF"

3. Select a junction box or outlet box on the problem circuit which has several wires leading in and out. CHECK WITH YOUR NEON CIRCUIT TESTER TO BE SURE THAT THE WIRES ARE NOT LIVE BEFORE TOUCHING ANY.

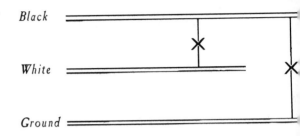

SHORT - CAUSED WHEN CONTACT IS MADE BETWEEN A BLACK AND A WHITE OR A BLACK AND A GROUND WIRE.

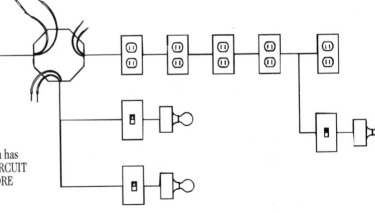

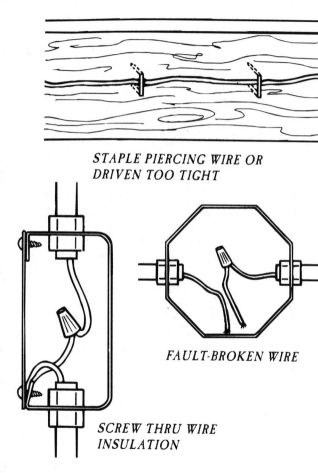

**STAPLE PIERCING WIRE OR
DRIVEN TOO TIGHT**

FAULT-BROKEN WIRE

**SCREW THRU WIRE
INSULATION**

TROUBLESHOOTING

4. Identify and mark all wires to aid in re-connecting them. Then separate them, making sure that they extend out of the box without touching anything.

5. Turn on the power at the main panel. If the power remains on, you have disconnected that part of the circuit with the fault. If the circuit breaker still trips or the fuse blows, the fault lies between that junction box and the main panel. You will need to locate a junction box closer to the main panel and test again.

6. If the power remains on, you need to identify which part of the disconnected circuit contains the fault. To do this use your neon circuit tester to find which pair of black and white wires are live. Turn off the power and reconnect the circuits one at a time. The one that causes the breaker to trip or the fuse to blow is the one with the problem.

7. When you have narrowed down the problem to a particular part of the circuit, examine all junction boxes and outlets carefully. Look for broken or loose wires touching each other or the metal box. Look also for mounting screws which may have cut through wire insulation. Examine ceiling fixtures, remembering not to let them hang by their wires. The trouble may also be caused by a staple which was driven through the wire or driven to tightly. Remove and test outlets with your continuity tester to see if they are shorted. If you're still not able to identify the problem, it is probably due to hidden damage and you should call your electrician.

TROUBLESHOOTING

Power losses- outlets OK, lighting circuits inoperative, or not working properly

If there is power on all parts of the circuit, but lights are inoperative and the bulbs test good, the problem may be a defective switch. The diagram on p. 69 shows you how to test various switches with the battery continuity tester after the switch has been removed from the wall. REMOVE FUSE OR TURN CIRCUIT BREAKER TO "OFF" before unwiring switches for testing.

If the circuit contains three-way or three-way and four way switches, and the light does not operate properly from all switch points, and the switches test good, the problem may be that the proper wire is not going to the common terminal on the three-way switch. The common terminal on a three-way is identified by the word "common" or by a color which is distinct from the other two screws. If you suspect that this is the problem,

the common wire can be identified as follows:

1. REMOVE FUSE OR TURN CIRCUIT BREAKER TO "OFF" Remove the three-way switch, position the three wires so that they are not next to each other or close to any metal of the box or other equipment.

2. Turn on the power and carefully check between each wire and the grounded metal box with a neon circuit tester. Make a note of the one wire that indicates that it is live.

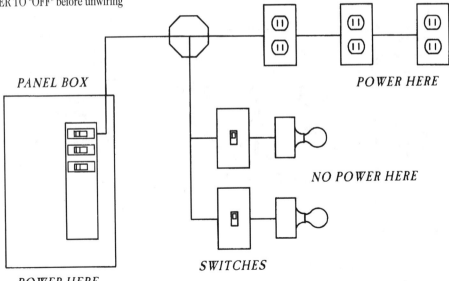

OUTLETS

POWER HERE

PANEL BOX

NO POWER HERE

SWITCHES

POWER HERE

3. Go to the other three-way switch and switch it to the other position.

4. Return to original switch and repeat the test as in step 2. If one wire s always live, and does not change when the other switch is thrown, this hould be connected to the common terminal of the switch. Or, if when he other switch if thrown, the second wire becomes live, then the third ire which was never live is the ommon wire.*

5. TURN THE CIRCUIT BREAKER O "OFF" OR REMOVE THE FUSE. onnect the common wire which you st identified to the terminal marked ommon" or the one with the different lor screw. Reconnect the other two ires to the remaining two screws. einstall the switch in the wall box, place the wall plate and turn on the wer. The switches should now perate properly.

*If no wires are live, TURN OFF OWER and reinstall the switch. epeat the above procedure at the her switch location.

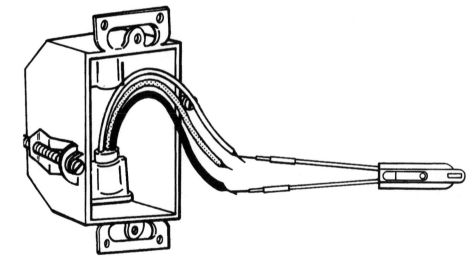

CIRCUIT DIAGRAMS

When troubleshooting difficult problems, it sometimes helps to know what path the electricity is supposed to take. The illustrations show typical circuit connections for switches and outlets.

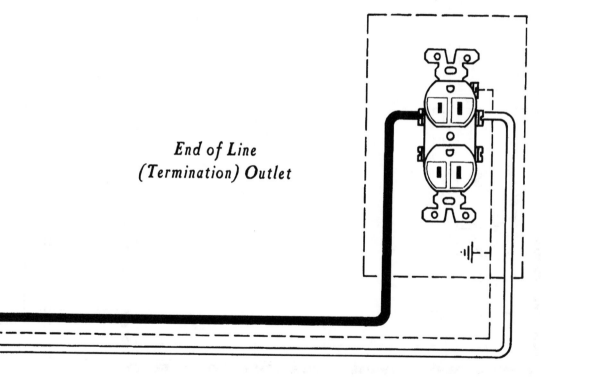

*End of Line
(Termination) Outlet*

CIRCUIT DIAGRAMS

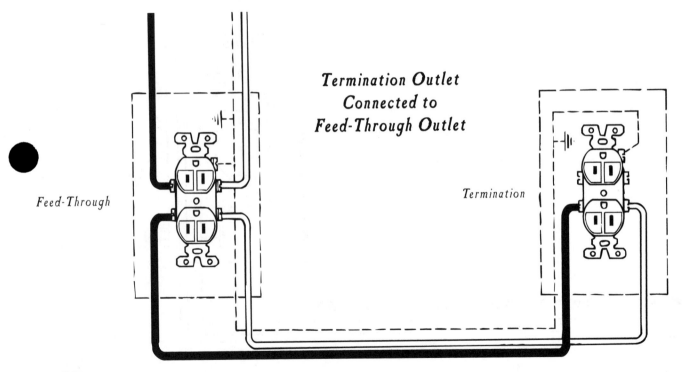

Termination Outlet
Connected to
Feed-Through Outlet

Feed-Through

Termination

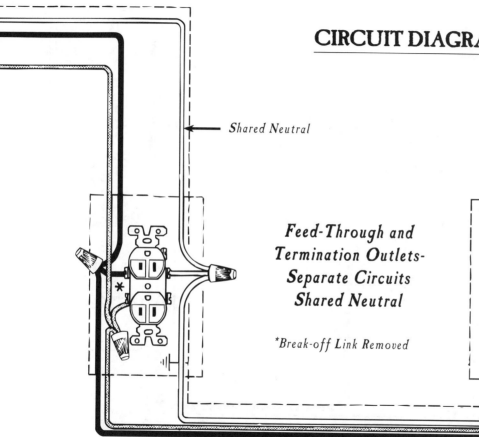

Shared Neutral

Feed-Through and Termination Outlets- Separate Circuits Shared Neutral

Break-off Link Removed

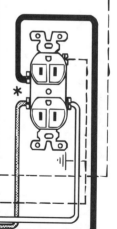

81

CIRCUIT DIAGRAMS

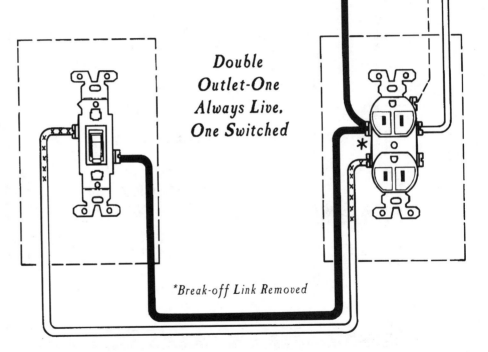

NOTE: NEUTRAL NOT
PRESENT IN SWITCH
BOX. PAINT WIRE
BLACK TO INDICATE
HOT OR LIVE.

*Double
Outlet-One
Always Live,
One Switched*

Break-off Link Removed

82

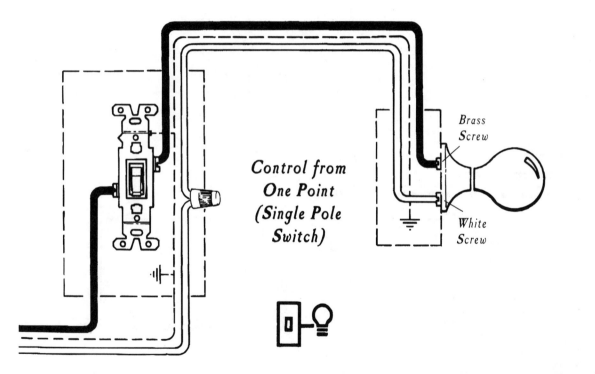

Control from
One Point
(Single Pole
Switch)

Brass
Screw

White
Screw

83

CIRCUIT DIAGRAMS

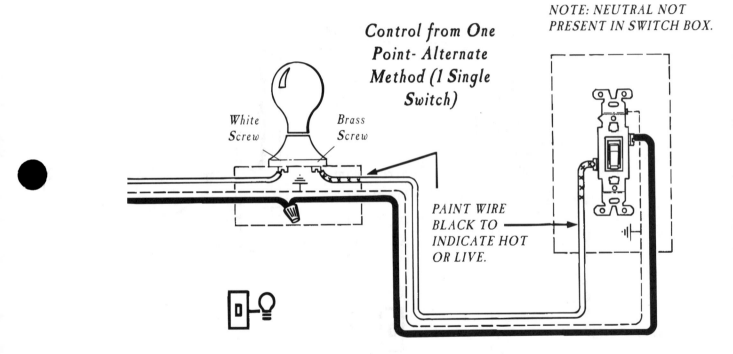

Control from One Point- Alternate Method (1 Single Switch)

NOTE: NEUTRAL NOT PRESENT IN SWITCH BOX.

White Screw

Brass Screw

PAINT WIRE BLACK TO INDICATE HOT OR LIVE.

84

CIRCUIT DIAGRAMS

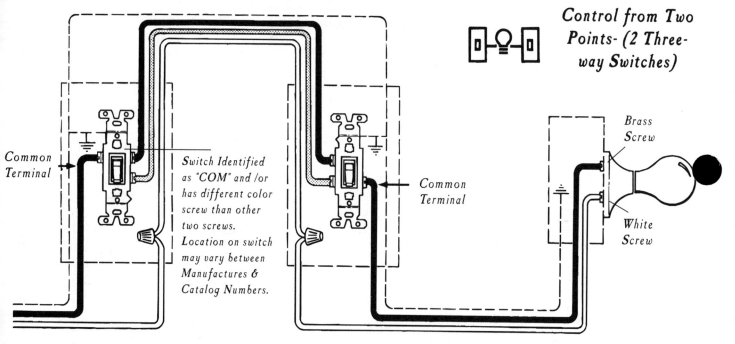

Control from Two Points- (2 Three-way Switches)

Common Terminal

Switch Identified as "COM" and /or has different color screw than other two screws. Location on switch may vary between Manufactures & Catalog Numbers.

Common Terminal

Brass Screw

White Screw

Note: "COMMON" Terminal Location Switch Varies. Look for Identification.

85

CIRCUIT DIAGRAMS

Control from Four Points- (2 Three-way Switches, Two Four-way Switches)

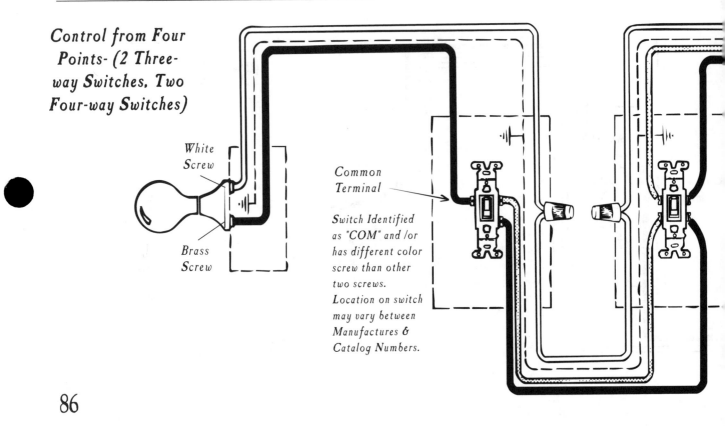

White Screw

Brass Screw

Common Terminal

Switch Identified as "COM" and /or has different color screw than other two screws. Location on switch may vary between Manufactures & Catalog Numbers.

CIRCUIT DIAGRAMS

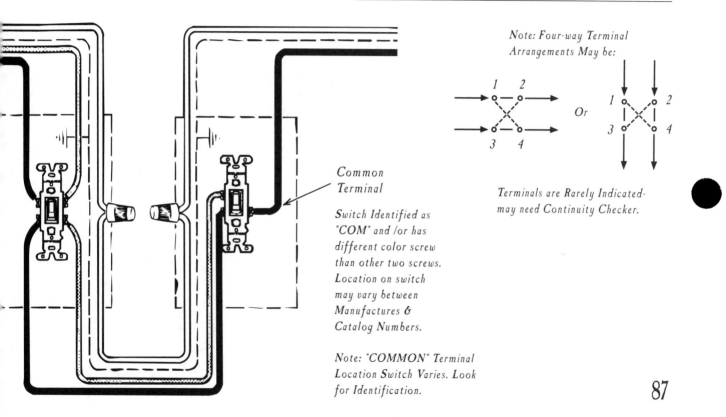

Note: Four-way Terminal
Arrangements May be:

Or

Terminals are Rarely Indicated-
may need Continuity Checker.

*Common
Terminal*

*Switch Identified as
"COM" and /or has
different color screw
than other two screws.
Location on switch
may vary between
Manufactures &
Catalog Numbers.*

*Note: "COMMON" Terminal
Location Switch Varies. Look
for Identification.*

87

INDEX

88

THIS SPACE FOR SKETCHES
OF YOUR HOME CIRCUITS

THIS SPACE FOR SKETCHES
OF YOUR HOME CIRCUITS

**THIS SPACE FOR SKETCHES
OF YOUR HOME CIRCUITS**

**THIS SPACE FOR SKETCHES
OF YOUR HOME CIRCUITS**

**THIS SPACE FOR SKETCHES
OF YOUR HOME CIRCUITS**

**THIS SPACE FOR SKETCHES
OF YOUR HOME CIRCUITS**

THIS SPACE FOR SKETCHES
OF YOUR HOME CIRCUITS

THIS SPACE FOR SKETCHES
OF YOUR HOME CIRCUITS

**THIS SPACE FOR SKETCHES
OF YOUR HOME CIRCUITS**